Men's Fitness
magazine

C000138134

TRAIN LIKE AN
OLYMPIAN

By Jon Lipsey

Additonal words Joe Warner, Joel Snape, Sam Rider
Design Ian Jackson, Scott Moore
Subeditor Juliet Giles
Photography Tom Miles, Naki Kouyioumtzis, Getty, Corbis, Shutterstock
Model Dave Norwell@WAthletic

© Copyright Dennis Publishing
Ltd. Licensed by Felden 2011 **MAGBOOK**

Publisher **Russell Blackman**
Managing Director **Ian Westwood**
Digital Production Manager **Nicky Baker**
MagBook Publisher **Dharmesh Mistry**
Operations Director **Robin Ryan**
Managing Director of Advertising
Julian Lloyd-Evans
Newstrade Director **David Barker**
Chief Operating Officer **Brett Reynolds**
Group Finance Director **Ian Leggett**
Chief Executive Officer **James Tye**
Chairman **Felix Dennis**

The 'MagBook' brand is a trademark of Dennis Publishing Ltd.
30 Cleveland St, London W1T 4JD. Company registered in England.
All material © Dennis Publishing Ltd, licensed by Felden 2011,
and may not be reproduced in whole or in part without the
consent of the publishers.

Train Like An Olympian ISBN 1-907779-80-9
To license this product please contact Hannah Heagney on
+44 (0) 20 7907 6134 or email hannah_heagney@dennis.co.uk
Printed at BGP, Bicester.

Advertising
Katie Wood katie_wood@dennis.co.uk
Matt Wakefield matt_wakefield@dennis.co.uk

CHANGE

TO A SUPERIOR PROTEIN

Instant Whey is unlike other whey proteins and the differences can deliver you significant benefits.

166% more bio available cystine, 16% more leucine
It uses Native Whey which is different to conventional whey protein having a less invasive pasteurising process. As a result it contains up to 166% more bio available cystine than conventional whey which is vital for optimal immune function and therefore recovery after exercise. It also contains up to 16% more leucine which helps to build and repair muscle.

It is unbeaten in terms of its protein levels at a guaranteed level of 80%. Containing a market leading protein percentage also means that it contains less fat and less carbohydrate.

Reflex Instant Whey inc. Native Whey	**80%**
Competitor brand A	78.5%
Competitor brand B	78%
Competitor brand C	76.6%
Competitor brand D	72%
Competitor brand E	70%

Delivering such a high quality product can only be achieved by controlling the entire manufacturing process and testing each batch produced. Not only does Reflex operate what is arguably the most advanced manufacturing unit in the UK but every single batch of Instant Whey is protein tested and the results published on our website.

Given our unique approach to quality we are able to offer a simple, no questions asked Full Money Back Guarantee (see website).

If you haven't tried Instant Whey recently, you owe it to yourself to do so. Not only is it unique in respect of the inclusion of Native Whey, market leading in terms of its protein percentage but it also comes in a range of fantastic flavours and is covered by a simple and effective guarantee.

This explains why we are inviting you to Change to a superior protein.

Instant Whey
inc. Native Whey

Part of our Higher Protein range

Find out more about our products at:

www.reflex-nutrition.com

reflex®
Tomorrow's Nutrition Today™

Contents

34

66

80

56

Who are you training with today?

SHAPE UP WITH L-CARNITINE LIQUID

AVAILABLE IN INDEPENDENT HEALTH FOOD STORES

SOLGAR VITAMIN AND HERB
essentials for life's journey
www.solgar.com/uk

Contents

104

134

116

BUILD A WINNING PHYSIQUE

Follow the plans of elite sportsmen to get a body that deserves a medal

In July and August this year, thousands of athletes will gather in London for the 2012 Summer Olympic Games. There may be a wide variety of sports but those competing have a lot in common. They've all dedicated their lives to their sports and, especially for the home athletes, it's going to be the biggest moment of their careers.

They also share the fact that their bodies have been honed so that they are able to do exactly what their sport requires. The 100m sprinters, for example, are muscular powerhouses, the road cyclists are lean endurance machines and the gymnasts combine incredible strength with complete control of their bodies.

This book is devoted to the training secrets that helped get those athletes into such incredible shape. And it doesn't come from an expert who talks a good game but has never performed at a decent level. No, it comes directly from the athletes who will be going for medals in London.

Going for gold

The book starts with a chapter covering the basics of training. That's because it makes sense to build a base level of fitness before you start your elite level training programme. The section covers how to warm up, how to build muscle, improve core strength and how to eat to help you hit your sporting targets.

The section on athletics (p52) starts with a routine from 400m hurdle world champion Dai Greene. That's followed by former triple jump world champion Phillips Idowu and there's a plan from rising discus star Lawrence Okoye, who looks like he has the potential to smash records. The chapter on rowing (p72) features programmes from Pete Reed and Andrew Hodge, both of whom have won Olympic gold medals. Their routines are intense strength builders. They're not easy but they'll help you pack on muscle. The world-beating advice continues with the aquatics section (p86), which covers drills from the world champion swimmer Liam Tancock and from diver Peter Waterfield – Tom Daley's partner. Both men require high levels of core strength so if it's a rippling six-pack you're after, they're the guys to copy. If you're into combat sports (p100), you'll enjoy the workouts from James DeGale, who won gold at the 2008 Olympics before turning pro and becoming British and then European supermiddleweight champion. We've also got an innovative

'It's the Olympic title that everyone wants. You can win everything else but if you haven't got an Olympic title you're not really recognised as one of the greats'

Linford Christie, Olympic 100m champion, 1992

routine from Britain's best judo player, Euan Burton. He recommends doing grip work, which is useful for his sport but also for anyone who finds that their grip lets them down when they're lifting weights. The cycling chapter (p112) includes drills from Olympic gold medal winner Ed Clancy and an exclusive interview with multiple gold medal winner Bradley Wiggins. One of our biggest gold medal hopes, Alistair Brownlee, spearheads the triathlon section (p120). He'll be under intense pressure to win gold but on his day he looks unbeatable. The final sport chapter (p130) features two young gymnasts, Daniel Keatings and Louis Smith, who are putting Britain on the map in that sport. And from the new generation of Olympic hopefuls we take a step back in sporting time to speak to five solid gold Olympic legends. We've got exclusive interviews with Linford Christie, Seb Coe, Steve Redgrave, Jonathan Edwards and Chris Boardman. Find out from them what it takes to win on the world's biggest sporting stage.

Winning moves

It's not just outstanding talent that links all of the athletes in this book. They also have a lot in common when it comes to their training programmes. And we're not just talking about the hours that they put in, but also the type of workouts that they do. If you analyse the sessions you'll notice that none of them spend much time doing isolation moves such as biceps curls. Instead they do a lot of multi-muscle group moves, such as squats and cleans. The reason they do those exercises is because they're the best way of building strength and explosive power. Generally, the stronger an athlete is, the better he will be at his sport. All athletes also need to generate strength at speed, which is where the power moves come in. And, of course, they need to have rock solid core muscles, so that none of their power is lost by having a weak mid-section. But you'll also notice that no one recommends doing crunches. Instead they do abs moves that require your entire trunk, and also some other muscle groups, to stabilise the movements.

Getting results

To see success with the workouts you should follow one routine for between four to six weeks. If you want to follow the same routine for longer than that, make sure that you alter some of the key variables, such as sets, reps and tempo, which are explained in Building A Workout (p31). That will give you enough time to make a difference but not so long that your body gets used to the programme. Once you're feeling confident you could even cherry pick the exercises you like from different sportsmen. Provided you follow the principles outlined in the programme design section of the training basics chapter, you'll create a useful workout. You could end up with a sprinter's legs, a boxer's abs, a rower's back, a swimmer's broad shoulders and a gymnast's arms.

The workouts in this book have got the athletes to the very top of their sports. Follow them and we're sure that you'll smash your own personal bests.

'The Olympics will always be special to me because it's where I started and where I've had most of my success. If I'm honest I'm getting a bit greedy. That's just part of the motivation, seeing how far you can push yourself'

Bradley Wiggins, six-time Olympic medal winning cyclist

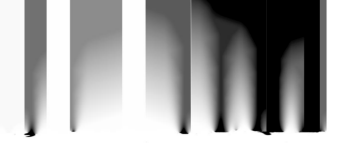

FOCUS ON YOUR GOALS. NOT YOUR FEET.

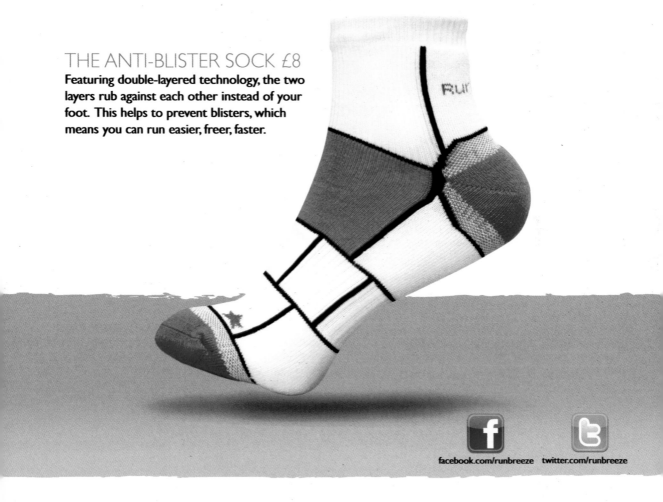

THE ANTI-BLISTER SOCK £8

Featuring double-layered technology, the two layers rub against each other instead of your foot. This helps to prevent blisters, which means you can run easier, freer, faster.

facebook.com/runbreeze   twitter.com/runbreeze

Get set to train ▶

MASTERING THE FUNDAMENTALS

Before you launch yourself into an elite level training programme you need to master the fitness fundamentals. This chapter will give you a good understanding about why you're training, what effect it will have on your muscles and the basic principles behind the sessions in this book.

WHY YOU NEED TO WORK OUT

Regular exercise will improve your body, your mind and your mood

You already instinctively know about the benefits of exercise – that being active makes you feel better, both physically and mentally – and there's plenty of scientific evidence to back up those instincts.

● Protect your heart
Weight training helps improve your cardiovascular health by widening your blood vessels, according to research published in the *Journal Of Strength And Conditioning Research*. The study also found that resistance exercise produced a longer lasting drop in blood pressure than a bout of aerobic exercise.

● Strengthen your bones
Weight training not only builds strong muscles, it also srengthens bones, according to a study published in the *Journal of Applied Physiology*. When you lift a weight your muscles pull on the tissues that connect them to your bones. This forces your body to increase the density of your bones, which will help prevent diseases, such as osteoporosis.

● Boost your brain
Exercise increases blood flow to your brain, which helps oxygen and nutrient delivery. Research from the University of Illinois found that people who exercise experience 'substantial sparing' from the natural decay of the parts of the brain that handle memory, problem solving and thinking.

● Burn more fat
Lifting weights on a regular basis raises your basal metabolic rate – the speed at which your body burns calories – so you'll burn more fat, according to the *Journal*

'Working out releases the feelgood hormones called endorphins'

of Applied Physiology. Strength training increases lean muscle mass and the more of this active tissue you have, the greater the number of calories it needs to function, helping to eat into your fat reserves.

● Ward off colds
Being fit can reduce your chances of getting colds, according to US researchers who monitored 1,002 adults for 12 weeks.

Those in the top 25 per cent of fitness levels experienced 43 per cent fewer days with upper respiratory tract illness than the least fit 25 per cent. When the fit group did get ill, their symptoms were, on average, 32 per cent less severe than the least fit group.

● Feel happier
Working out releases the feelgood hormones called endorphins and there is even evidence that exercise can help treat mild depression. In a study published in the journal *Psychosomatic Medicine*, 45 per cent of depressed subjects who participated in group exercise, and 40 per cent who worked out at home, saw their symptoms recede.

● Perk up your sex life
Weight training can do wonders for your sex life, and not just because women will be swooning over your new muscular body. Exercise increases your physical endurance and improves blood flow around the body, according to research from the University of Arkansas. And you don't need a degree in physiology to work out why that's a good thing.

● Reduce the risk of disease
Regular exercise can significantly reduce your risk of a number of serious illnesses, including diabetes, stroke and some cancers, especially that of the colon. US studies have shown that those who exercise have a 30-40 per cent smaller risk of developing colon cancer than those who are sedentary.

ESSENTIAL TRAINING TIPS

Whatever sport you're training for don't start your workout programme until you've read these easy-to-adopt nuggets of workout advice

• Keep a record
Every Olympian keeps a detailed record of their training sessions. You too should record what you've done, what you've lifted, and what was happening outside of training. Knowing you had a bad day at work, for example, can help explain why training went badly.

• Be realistic
Be ambitious, yes, but if your aim is to compete in the 2016 Olympics you're setting yourself up for a fall. Stick to something you can commit to, such as three training sessions a week. You can always add a session once your habits are established.

• Short can be sweet
Olympians may train for hours every day, but you'll get great benefits from comparatively short but intense sessions, which are more productive than hours spent on the treadmill. You can cut your gym time in half by reducing rest and increasing intensity.

• Work on flexibility
Full-time athletes don't have trouble finding time to train. But the rest of us need to work training around work and family commitments. Plan in advance but if you know you've got a busy week at work, back off a bit. When you get more free time, you can put in more training.

• Don't get legless
Unless you're a sprinter it's tempting to neglect your legs. But if you don't do squats, lunges and deadlifts you won't build muscle and lose fat effectively – and will end up with pencil legs. As well as working your legs, squats help release growth hormone to increase muscle all over your body.

• Stay positive
The right frame of mind can make a huge difference to the effectiveness of your workouts. Remind yourself on your way to the gym why you started the plan, and think how good you'll feel once you have reached your goals.

• Keep your core tight
Before any heavy lift, tighten your core muscles – those around your midriff – to protect your lower back from injury. Don't try and compensate for weak abs by wearing a weightlifters' belt. You're better to pick a lighter weight and build up slowly as your core strength increases.

• Time your sets
Each set of each exercise should take you around 40-45 seconds to complete. Any faster and you're not putting your muscles under tension long enough to get good results. So, each rep should take three or four seconds. Make the lowering (eccentric) portion of the lift slow and controlled, and then move powerfully through the exertion (concentric) part.

• Don't forget to breathe
Never hold your breath during a heavy lift. Instead the general rule is to breathe in as you lower the weight, and then breathe out through pursed lips as you lift the weight.

• Stay balanced
Do as many lower-body moves as upper-body; for every pushing motion do a pulling one; and give the same amount of attention to opposing muscle groups, such as biceps and triceps.

• Be progressive
Aim to increase the resistance you use for an exercise by around ten per cent every three or four weeks. This will ensure that your muscles get the stimulation they need to grow. If the weights don't get bigger then neither will your muscles.

• Get your rest
Your muscles don't grow in the gym. They grow when they are recovering afterwards. That's why you shouldn't train the same muscle groups two days in a row, because they won't have had time to repair themselves from the first workout by the time you hit them again. If you want more muscle, always take rest days and make sure you get enough sleep.

• If it hurts – stop!
Pain is your body's way of telling you something is wrong, so if you feel any pain stop immediately and don't resume training until you've recovered. Always check with your GP if you are unsure whether you should train or not.

'Aim to increase the resistance you use for an exercise by around ten per cent every few weeks'

TRAINING MYTHS

MYTH

You can turn fat into muscle

Reality To convert fat into muscle you'd have to be an alchemist. They're two totally different things, so converting one into the other would be messing with all known laws of science. The process of building muscle and burning fat is unrelated. Muscle is active tissue that burns calories, while fat tissues store excess energy.

MYTH

Doing crunches builds a six-pack

Reality You can have the strongest abs in the world but if they're under a layer of fat then you're not going to see them. And if you're trying to burn fat, crunches are just about the worst move you could choose. In fact, you'd have to do about 500,000 to burn one kilogram of fat.

MYTH

Machines are better than free weights

Reality If they cost a lot of money and are constantly being updated, machines must be more useful than dumb-bells and barbells, right? Wrong. Machines only allow you to move in a fixed movement. That means your stabilising muscles, the ones that protect your joints, aren't forced to work, and if these are weak you increase your injury risk when you go from using machines to free weights.

GET INTO GEAR

Getting the right gear will help you perform like an elite athlete

£26 Adidas London 2012 Performance T-shirt

This lightweight training shirt is great for running, gym sessions and a variety of sports. Under arm panels use ClimaCool technology to improve breathability and keep you dry, while the three stripes gradient print gives it a stylish finish.
● **adidas.com**

£24 Adidas London 2012 Shorts

These multi-purpose shorts are ideal for a variety of sporting activities. An elasticated waistband provides a comfortable fit, while the use of ClimaCool, heat-reactive fabric on the legs ensures that you stay cooler and drier for longer.
● **adidas.com**

£65 Adidas AdiZero F50 Trainer

This trainer has a minimalist design and EVA outsole to keep it fast and light. The mixed fabric upper and external heel counter provide plenty of flexibility and durability too, making this shoe a staple for anyone's kit bag.
● **adidas.com**

BUILD YOUR OWN HOME GYM

Get this sporty home set-up for less than £90

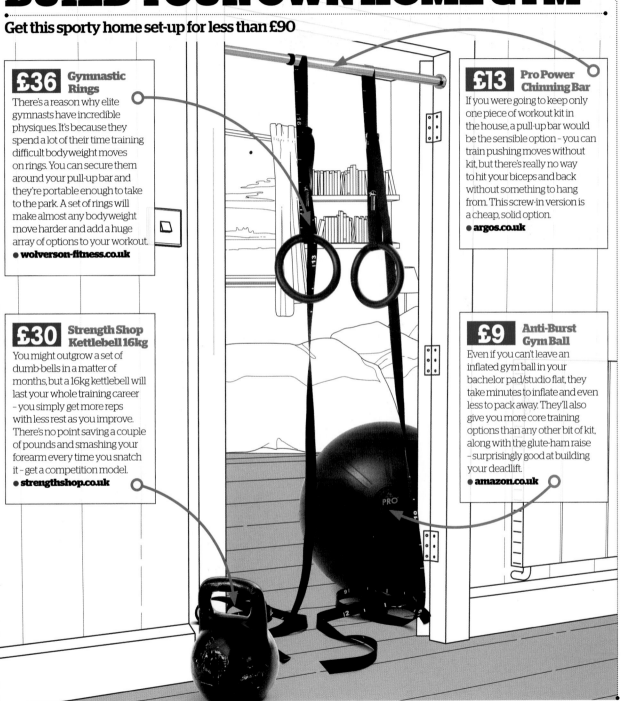

£36 Gymnastic Rings

There's a reason why elite gymnasts have incredible physiques. It's because they spend a lot of their time training difficult bodyweight moves on rings. You can secure them around your pull-up bar and they're portable enough to take to the park. A set of rings will make almost any bodyweight move harder and add a huge array of options to your workout.

● **wolverson-fitness.co.uk**

£30 Strength Shop Kettlebell 16kg

You might outgrow a set of dumb-bells in a matter of months, but a 16kg kettlebell will last your whole training career – you simply get more reps with less rest as you improve. There's no point saving a couple of pounds and smashing your forearm every time you snatch it – get a competition model.

● **strengthshop.co.uk**

£13 Pro Power Chinning Bar

If you were going to keep only one piece of workout kit in the house, a pull-up bar would be the sensible option – you can train pushing moves without kit, but there's really no way to hit your biceps and back without something to hang from. This screw-in version is a cheap, solid option.

● **argos.co.uk**

£9 Anti-Burst Gym Ball

Even if you can't leave an inflated gym ball in your bachelor pad/studio flat, they take minutes to inflate and even less to pack away. They'll also give you more core training options than any other bit of kit, along with the glute-ham raise – surprisingly good at building your deadlift.

● **amazon.co.uk**

PRE-WORKOUT WARM-UP

Do this routine before every workout to prepare your body and prevent injury

A proper warm-up is vital before doing any weight training. If time is short, don't be tempted to skip the warm-up and go straight to your workout, because cold muscles can get easily damaged. A few minutes saved on a warm-up can mean days lost while recovering from injury.

DYNAMIC STRETCHES | 10 reps of each

1 Lunge with reverse flye

- Step forward while stretching your arms to the sides.
- Keep your body upright.
- Lunge lower with each rep.

2 Lateral lunge with twist

- Step to the side with both feet pointing forwards.
- Twist your torso in the direction of your leading foot.
- Bend your knee a bit further with each rep.

Your warm-up should start with some light cardiovascular exercise, such as running, rowing or cycling. This will make your heart beat faster, pumping oxygen and nutrients to your muscles, and elevating your body's core temperature. Warm muscles are more elastic than cold ones, which allows you to work them through a greater range of motion with less injury.

After the cardio you then need to target your muscles directly with dynamic stretches. These differ from static stretches in that you are moving as you stretch out the muscle (see examples below). The trick is to start very gently and then slowly increase the range of motion you use with each repetition. This prepares your muscles and joints for the work to come.

Finally, before you begin any lifting exercise, perform the movements with minimal weight to teach your muscles how to respond when you do the exercise with full weights.

WARMING DOWN

> It's important after your final set to warm down before beginning your post-workout stretches (see next page). Warming down is the process of reducing your heart rate from its elevated state during the main part of you session and bringing down your core body temperature. Spend five to ten minutes performing some gentle cardio, gradually reducing the intensity every minute to help your body closer to its resting state.

3 Alternating split deadlift

● Step forward with one foot and lean forwards at the hips.
● Keep your back straight.
● Lower your hands down your shins a bit further each time, before pushing back to the start.

4 Squat to overhead reach

● Stand with feet shoulder-width apart and your back straight.
● Squat down and then reach overhead as you stand up.
● Squat a bit lower with each rep.

POST-WORKOUT STRETCHES

Static stretches are where you hold a muscle under tension while relaxing it in order to lengthen the muscle after it has contracted as a result of weight training. Performing static stretches after a workout

Ease your tired muscles after every workout

STATIC STRETCHES hold each for 20-30 seconds

1 Calves ● Push down on your rear heel.

2 Hamstrings ● Lean forward at the hips with a straight back.

3 Quads ● Pull on your ankle and push your hips forward.

7 Abs ● Lift your shoulders high off the floor.

8 Lats ● Press your shoulder towards the floor.

9 Lower back ● Keep your shoulders flat on the floor.

provides several benefits. First, it will help with flexibility, so you'll be able to work your muscles across a greater range of motion, leading to better muscle gains. Stretching also helps reduce injuries because your muscles and tendons are less likely to tear when they are relaxed.

Stretching improves blood flow to your muscles, helping to flush out toxins, meaning you'll be ready for your next workout sooner. And stretching can also aid posture,

because tense muscles can pull your spine, shoulders and hips out of alignment, leading to a stooped look and lower back pain.

It's important for your muscles that they are always fully warmed up before you perform any static stretches, so you should never do them as part of your warm-up at the beginning of a workout. Also, in order to avoid injury, don't pull too hard when you stretch, and don't 'bounce' the muscle under tension.

> 'Stretching improves blood flow to your muscles, helping to flush out toxins'

4 Hip flexors ● Keep your body upright and push your hips forward.

5 Adductors ● Press your knees apart gently with your elbows.

6 Glutes ● Gently pull on your knee.

10 Chest ● Press your hands backwards with straight arms.

11 Traps ● Pull gently on your head.

12 Triceps ● Point your fingers down your back and pull gently on your elbow.

13 Biceps ● Press your arms back while twisting your hands so your thumbs point behind you.

HOW MUSCLES WORK

Here's how the muscles you'll be targeting work and get bigger

Your body is a clever old thing and the process of muscle growth is, essentially, your body responding to the stress of weight training by thinking, 'that was hard, I better do something about it so it's not as difficult next time'.

That's because when you perform resistance exercises you create microscopic tears in your muscles. Your body then responds to this 'microtrauma' of the muscle cells by overcompensating, which means that the damaged tissue is repaired and more is added, so your muscles become bigger and stronger and the risk of future damage is minimised. This also means that you need to progressively increase the weight you lift, because your muscles quickly adapt to deal with the stress.

It is thought that this damage to your muscle fibres is the reason for delayed onset muscle soreness (DOMS), the symptoms of which are muscle soreness and stiffness in the days after a tough workout. That's why you should leave at least 48 hours between sessions that target the same muscle group. If you train again before your muscles have been repaired, you won't be as strong and risk injury and overtraining.

There are several key stages in the process that breaks down muscle fibres before they can be rebuilt.

The warm-up

● An increased heart rate pumps blood to your muscles, warming them up and allowing them to extend fully. It also supplies muscle fibres with oxygen.

Loading the muscle

● At the start of the rep your muscles are under load and stretched. As a result the heart pumps more blood into the protective sheaths that surround the muscle fibres, supplying oxygen and nutrients to these fibres.

Sparking your nervous system

● When you lift the weight your central nervous system relays this to the nerves contained in the sheaths protecting the muscle fibres. This tells the muscle fibres to contract, lifting the weight. If you're doing the exercise correctly, your muscles activate in a particular sequence and your central nervous system adapts to this. As you repeat the workout over time, your nerves get more efficient, allowing you to do more reps or lift more weight. This is the first adaptation caused by weightlifting.

Chemical reactions

● Adenosine triphosphate (ATP) is the immediate energy source for muscle contraction. It is broken down within the body's cells to release energy. The cells' creatine, phosphate and glycogen reserves are also converted into ATP. This process creates lactic acid as an unfortunate by-product.

Feeling the burn

● Once the glycogen stores in the cells are depleted and lactic acid builds up, the muscle can't work efficiently, so you take a rest. As you rest, aerobic (oxygen-based) muscle respiration occurs, processing the lactic acid back into glycogen and giving you an energy source for the next set.

Successful failure

● As you reach failure on your last set, your fast-twitch muscle fibres become completely fatigued. Microscopic tears ('microtears') are created in the myofilaments, the smallest fibre bundles in your muscles.

Repair and growth

● Your body repairs the microtears by adding the amino acids actin and myosin to the myofilaments, which also causes them to grow in size. The body is unable to grow additional muscle cells, so growth is limited by the number of cells that you have. Another effect of intense workouts is that your muscles adapt to store more glycogen, so that there will be more energy on hand for the next workout. This will also cause the muscles to increase in size slightly.

KNOW YOUR MUSCLES

There are more than 600 muscles in the human body. These are the major ones you'll be targeting during your workouts

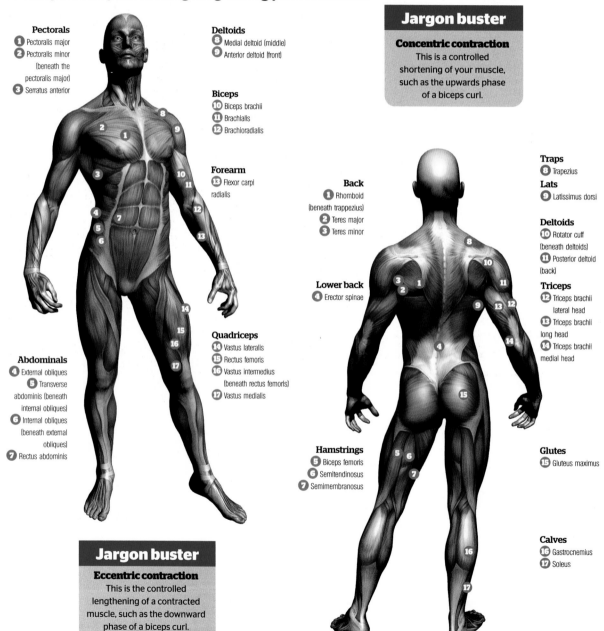

Pectorals
1 Pectoralis major
2 Pectoralis minor (beneath the pectoralis major)
3 Serratus anterior

Deltoids
8 Medial deltoid (middle)
9 Anterior deltoid (front)

Biceps
10 Biceps brachii
11 Brachialis
12 Brachioradialis

Forearm
13 Flexor carpi radialis

Abdominals
4 External obliques
5 Transverse abdominis (beneath internal obliques)
6 Internal obliques (beneath external obliques)
7 Rectus abdominis

Quadriceps
14 Vastus lateralis
15 Rectus femoris
16 Vastus intermedius (beneath rectus femoris)
17 Vastus medialis

Back
1 Rhomboid (beneath trappezius)
2 Teres major
3 Teres minor

Lower back
4 Erector spinae

Hamstrings
5 Biceps femoris
6 Semitendinosus
7 Semimembranosus

Traps
8 Trapezius

Lats
9 Latissimus dorsi

Deltoids
10 Rotator cuff (beneath deltoids)
11 Posterior deltoid (back)

Triceps
12 Triceps brachii lateral head
13 Triceps brachii long head
14 Triceps brachii medial head

Glutes
15 Gluteus maximus

Calves
16 Gastrocnemius
17 Soleus

Jargon buster
Concentric contraction
This is a controlled shortening of your muscle, such as the upwards phase of a biceps curl.

Jargon buster
Eccentric contraction
This is the controlled lengthening of a contracted muscle, such as the downward phase of a biceps curl.

'As soon as you lift a weight,
even if it's only once, you've
completed a rep and a set'

BUILDING A WORKOUT

How to create the perfect session to meet your fitness goals

The type of workout, you choose depends on whether your aim is to build a stronger, faster or leaner body. Before we take a closer look at the major workout protocols, let's examine the key components of every workout and how tweaking each one is vital to ensuring your progress continues unabated.

● The basics

A workout is comprised of a number of different elements or variables:

Exercise selection – the lifts you select to perform in any given workout.

Reps – an abbreviation of repetition, one rep is the completion of a given exercise from start to finish.

Sets – a set is a given number of reps performed consecutively without rest. The number of reps per set can vary from one to more than 20, depending on training goals.

Weight – the amount of resistance you lift for each set.

Tempo – the speed at which you perform each rep.

Rest – the amount of time you rest between sets and between exercises.

● The joy of sets

Sets and reps are the bread and butter of your workout. In fact you can't weight train without them. As soon as you lift a weight, even if it's only once, you've completed a rep and a set. But that's not necessarily the best method for you. Instead you need to lift a weight a certain number of times, rest for a given amount of time, then repeat this process a certain number of times. How many reps you perform per set depends entirely on your fitness goals.

● Picking the right rep range

1-5 reps

Training aim Increase in muscle strength and power.

Target weight 85-100% of one-rep max*.

Why? Low-rep sets of heavy weights build strength and power because they recruit, work and fatigue your fast-twitch muscle fibres (those responsible for short bursts of power as in sprinting). They are responsible for your muscles' explosiveness and this approach makes them grow back bigger. This rep range also improves the communication pathway between your brain and the muscle, enabling it to react and contract more quickly and with more force.

6-8 reps

Training aim Optimal compromise between an increase in muscle strength and size.

Target weight 78-83% of one-rep max.

Why? Sets in this rep range will still work your fast-twitch muscle fibres and improve the brain-muscle connection, but performing extra reps will fatigue your muscles more thoroughly, resulting in improvements in strength and size.

9-12 reps

Training aim Increased muscle mass and improved strength.

Target weight 70-77% of one-rep max.

Why? The most effective way to build muscle mass is for each set to last between 40 and 70 seconds. Sets of nine to 12 reps are the perfect rep range for this because the weight is heavy enough to fatigue the muscles thoroughly but still manageable for you to maintain correct form for the desired length of time.

13+ reps

Training aim Increase in muscle strength-endurance with some mass gains.

Target weight 60-69% of one-rep max.

Why? Lighter weights for a higher reps recruit, work and fatigue your slow-twitch fibres (those used in endurance sports, such as marathon running). Sets in this rep range improve the ability of these fibres to deal with lactic acid and the other waste products that accumulate during exercise. You will still see some muscle mass gains, however, especially if you are new to weight training.

*Note that all percentages are only guiding values since the relationship between the maximum and sub-maximum loads is influenced by training status, muscle group and exercise. Rep ranges taken from *German Body Comp Program* by Charles Poliquin (charlespoliquin.com).

MAKE A CHANGE

Keep muscles guessing and growing

Training out is all about change. Of course, the whole point is to change your body into a lean, mean, sporting machine, and the best way to achieve this is to regularly change your workouts.

That's not to say that the basic three sets of eight to 12 reps approach doesn't work: it does. But if you keep changing your workout methods you keep challenging your muscles in new and effective ways. Exercise the weight you select to lift are the two most important variables to change regularly, but tampering and tweaking with the other key variables can also have a big impact.

● Tempo

Tempo is the speed at which you lift and lower a weight during each rep. The slower the tempo, the longer your muscles are exposed to the stress of managing the weight. This is called 'time under tension'. The more damage you can do to your muscles during a session, the bigger and stronger they will grow back. Performing each rep very quickly can help build explosive power, but only if you maintain perfect form throughout otherwise you risk injury.

● Rest

Rest between sets and exercises allows your muscles to replenish their energy stores. Not resting for long enough means your muscles won't be as capable of performing the set with good form. Resting for too long can result in you not testing your muscles enough to force them to grow back bigger and stronger.

● Periodisation

Structuring your training programme into progressively more challenging phases is known as periodisation. How you structure this periodisation depends on your goal. So, if for example you want greater strength and hypertrophy (bigger muscles), keep sets and reps the same but increase the weight. Don't increase the load week by more than 2.5 per cent each week for upper-body moves or five per cent for lower-body exercises. Include a rest week at the end of each cycle of weekly load increases. Cycles can last between two and 12 weeks, but four to six is likely to give you the best results.

● Training frequency

Time away from training is vital when trying to improve fitness levels muscle because it's during these periods that your muscles are repaired and become bigger and stronger.

Too little rest between workouts means your muscles won't have fully recovered, so you may struggle to lift the same weights for the same sets and reps as before.

Too much rest between workouts means you are won't be pushing your muscles at the required intensity or giving them sufficient stimulus to grow.

● Failure

Training to failure is a strategy in which you're unable to lift the weight with correct form on the final rep of your set. This form of overload training shocks your muscles into growing back bigger or stronger.

Because it is so taxing on your muscles and central nervous system, you need adequate rest between sessions to allow a full recovery. Failure to do so will quickly result in overtraining, muscle soreness and even size and strength losses.

> 'Time away from training is vital when trying to improve fitness levels'

SESSION PLANNER

How you structure each session depends on your goals

There are many different ways to put your exercises, sets, reps and the other variables together to make up a workout. Here are the three main sessions structures.

● Circuit training

This type of session is popular with many people because it allows them to work their whole body in a short space of time. That's because circuit training is a variety of different moves or stations – anywhere between five and 12 exercises – performed back-to-back without rest. After all the stations have been completed you rest for up to three minutes before repeating the circuit again, typically doing three or four full circuits in one session.

The quick pace and constant switching between exercises and equipment shocks your body and tackles all your major muscle groups, meaning you can get an effective full-body workout in as little as 45 minutes. The intensive nature of this session means that you won't be lifting heavy weights – some stations may only be bodyweight moves – so circuits are better suited for building muscular endurance, burning fat and a decent aerobic workout than for adding serious muscle mass.

● Total Body Training

A total body routine involves training every major muscle group each time you hit the gym. So you'd perform one body-part specific move for a certain number of sets and reps before moving on to another body part.

A typical workout might look like this:
Bench press (chest and triceps)
Bent-over row (upper back and biceps)
Squats (legs)
Good morning (lower back)
Shoulder press (shoulders and triceps)
Crunch and plank (abs and core)

● Split training

Split – or body part – training involves working specific muscle groups in one session, then focusing on another group of muscles in the next workout. This approach allows you to fully exhaust certain muscles one day, before giving them several days to recover before training them again, during which time you can train other muscle groups.

A typical split routine may look like this:
Day one Chest and back
Day two Legs
Day three Rest
Day four Arms and shoulders
Day five Rest, before repeating from day one.

READY TO LIFT

Use compound lifts for better sports performance

W hen planning a training programme, compound lifts should form the backbone of each session. That's because this type of lift is far more effective at getting the different muscles of your body used to working together as a single unit. The more coordinated your muscles are, the faster, stronger and more powerful you will be on the track, field or whatever your sporting arena. This will ultimately result in greater success.

So what exactly is a compound exercise? Put simply, it is a lift where there is movement at two or more different joints. A good example would be the squat (movement at the hip and knee joints) or shoulder press (movement at the shoulder and elbow joints). The other type of lift is an isolation move, where movement is limited to one joint only. An example of this type of move would be a biceps curl (movement at the elbow joint only).

Compound interest
Because compound lifts involve movement at more than one joint they require multiple muscle groups to act at the same time. Compound lifts are more-bang-for-buck moves because the more muscles involved, the heavier the weight you can lift, which results in a bigger growth-hormone response so your body will burn more fat while adding more muscle, giving you the best body for sporting excellence.

● Deadlift

WHY? Picking something up off the floor is a primal movement and the deadlift will strengthen every muscle in your posterior chain – the often neglected muscles at the back of your body.

HOW? Grasp a bar with hands shoulder width apart with your knees bent, your chest up and your weight on your heels. Push through your heels to straighten your legs and stand up without rounding your back.

● Shoulder press

WHY? This is a useful movement in everyday life and lifting a heavy weight overhead is also one of the best core strengthening movements.

HOW? Rest the bar on the top of the front of your chest then press it directly overhead.

● Squat

WHY? This is the most effective exercise you can do to strengthen your legs and it'll also develop your core.

HOW? Rest the bar on your shoulders then bend at the knees and the hips to lower towards the floor while keeping your torso upright. Lower until your thighs are at least parallel to the floor then push through your heels to straighten your legs.

● Bench press

WHY? This is a classic test of upper-body strength and, if done properly, becomes a whole body exercise.

HOW? Lie on the bench with your feet jammed into the floor behind the line of your knees. Start with the bar directly above your chest then lower it under control. When you push up, squeeze your glutes, push your feet into the ground and make your entire torso solid. The more stable you are, the more weight you'll be able to lift.

● Bent-over row

WHY? This will develop the muscles of your back while also recruiting your glutes and core to stabilise the movement.

HOW? Unlock your knees and bend at the hips, rather than the waist, so that the bar hangs straight down. Row the bar up to your sternum, keeping your elbows high and squeezing your shoulder blades together at the top of the move.

LIFT BIGGER

Perfecting the two Olympic lifts primes your body for any sport

The grunting and the gurning involved with Olympic lifting means the sport is sometimes thought of as being a source of comedy. But apart from the 100m it's hard to think of a purer form of athletic capacity. The snatch is the challenge to lift as much weight was possible from the floor to above your head in one multi-faceted movement. The clean and jerk is also a test to lift as much weight as possible from the floor to above your head – but this time with a pause before the jerk phase of the exercise.

Why you should do the Olympic lifts

The Olympic lifts are a glorious, red-faced combination of technique, strength and power. They're also immensely useful for anyone who wants to get better at their chosen sport. The Olympic lifts teach you to coordinate your body under load and stress. When you then do the big lifts you'll be confident that your body knows how to create success with the weight you're trying to lift.

SNATCH

Perfect your form for this classic lift

1 Start position
● Start with your feet hip-width apart and your knees flared towards your elbows. Grip the bar so that when it's overhead there is around 15cm between your head and the bar.
● Keep your back flat, your shoulders over the bar, your knees in front of the bar with the bar pressed into your shins.
● Keep your head up, looking straight ahead, take a deep breath and take the tension of the bar.

2 Pull to knees
● Pull the bar up in a smooth movement at a pace that maintains the tightness of the back but still generates good speed. Allow the bar to travel straight up, keeping it close to your legs.
● The initial pull should get you into a position that looks like a Romanian deadlift, legs straight but still soft at the knee.
● Make sure that the shoulders are over the bar at all times.

3 Pull to hips
● Stand up straight so that you rise up onto your toes. At this point your arms should still be straight.
● Make sure your shoulders are still in front of the bar and try to 'kick' the bar with the top of your thighs.

4 The drop
● The key to executing this part of the move is to make sure you have momentum from the hip extension.
● Bend your elbows, allowing them to rotate behind the body.
● At the same time, lift your knees so your feet leave the floor then stamp your feet into a squat position with your feet just over hip-width apart.
● Snap your arms straight overhead.

5 Recovery
● Stand up straight without locking out your knees and hips then lower the bar to prepare for the next rep.

STEP 1 · STEP 2 · STEP 3 · STEP 4 · STEP 6

CLEAN AND JERK

Learn to lift heavier with this classic technique

1 Start position
● Start with your feet hip-width apart and your knees flared towards your elbows.
● Grip the bar just wider than shoulder-width apart.
● Keep your back flat, your shoulders over the bar, your knees in front of the bar with the bar pressed into your shins.
● Keep your head up, looking straight ahead, take a deep breath and take the tension of the bar.

2 Pull to knees
● Pull the bar up in a smooth movement at a pace that maintains the tightness of the back but still generates good speed. Allow the bar to travel straight up, keeping it close to your legs.
● The initial pull should get you into a position that looks like a Romanian deadlift, legs straight but still soft at the knee.
● Make sure that the shoulders are over the bar at all times.

3 Pull to hips
● Stand up straight so you rise up on to your toes. At this point your arms should still be straight.
● Make sure your shoulders are still in front of the bar and try to 'kick' the bar with the top of your thighs.

STEP 1   STEP 2   STEP 3   STEP 4

4 The drop
● The key to executing this part of the move is to make sure you have momentum from the hip extension.
● Bend your elbows, allowing them to rotate behind the body. At the same time, lift your knees so your feet leave the floor then stamp your feet into a squat position with your feet just over hip-width apart.
● Allow the bar to land on the shoulders with the elbow pushed high.

5 Recovery and jerk set
● Stand up straight without locking out your knees and hips.
● Lower your elbows until they are directly under the bar then take a deep breath.
● Make sure your weight is on your heels.

6 Dip and drive
● Dip steadily by bending your knees but make sure it's fast enough to create a bounce in a very shallow and upright squat.
● Jump up on to your toes explosively.

7 Split and recover
● Drop underneath the bar into an overhead split squat.
● Make sure you really bend your back knee and come up on to your back toes.
● For extra stability, turn in the front foot slightly.
● Stand up, without locking out your knees and hips, before lowering the bar to prepare for the next rep.

STEP 5

STEP 6

STEP 7

SUPER CIRCUITS

If you're struggling to find the time to squeeze your sessions into an already busy schedule, then circuit training could be the answer

Circuit training – performing anywhere between five and 12 exercises back-to-back without rest – is popular with many people because it allows them to work their whole body in a short space of time.

Once you've finished all the exercises (more commonly known as stations), you rest for up to three minutes before repeating the circuit from the beginning again, typically doing three or four circuits in one session.

The quick pace and constant switching between exercises mean your muscles get a workout while you also push your cardiovascular fitness to the max,

which is the perfection preparation for the intensive nature of all sports.

The main advantages of circuit training are that it works the whole body in a short space of time; provides an aerobic workout, builds muscular endurance and burns fat; it can be done anywhere, at any time, using bodyweight exercises; and has great transfer value to sports performance.

Because these workouts are so demanding you won't be lifting heavy weights – in fact the example right uses just bodyweight moves – so they're better suited for building muscular endurance, burning fat and providing an aerobic workout than adding muscle mass.

'The quick pace and constant switching between exercises mean you get a muscle and cardio workout'

1 Lunge
● Take a big step forwards and plant your foot. Bend both knees until your front knee is at 90°.
● Keep your torso upright throughout the move and push through your front foot to get back to the start.

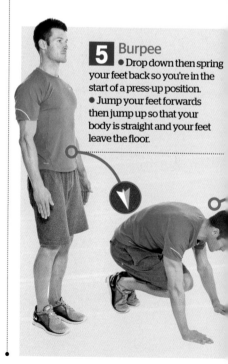

5 Burpee
● Drop down then spring your feet back so you're in the start of a press-up position.
● Jump your feet forwards then jump up so that your body is straight and your feet leave the floor.

2 Press-up
● Position your hands just wider than shoulder width apart with your body straight from head to heels.
● Bend your elbows to lower your torso to the floor, keeping your elbows in to your sides.

3 Squat
● Bend at the knees and the hips to lower towards the floor while keeping your torso upright.
● Lower until your thighs are at least parallel to the floor then push through your heels to straighten your legs.

4 Inverted shoulder press
● Place your feet on a chair and your hands on the floor with your arms straight and your body forming an inverted V.
● Bend your elbows to lower your head to the floor then press back up.

CORE STRENGTH AND STABILITY

Build a solid midsection and reap the rewards

A solid core is more than just about having an impressive six-pack. It offers many more benefits than just looking good, especially when optimal athletic performance is your goal.

Your core is comprised of your abdominals, internal and external obliques, erector spinae and many other deep lying muscles. One of its main roles is to stabilise your torso during all dynamic movements: if your body isn't in a stable position then your muscles won't be able to fire as effectively, resulting in poor power output.

For sportsmen, the other key benefit of a strong and stable core is that you can transfer power between your upper and lower body – and vice versa – more efficiently. And by doing so you allow all your muscles to work together as a single unit so you can exert maximum force, whether you're sprinting, jumping or throwing. Plus the stronger your core, the heavier you'll be able to lift, and so the greater your muscle gains.

▼ Lunge rotation

Stand with core braced and hands locked together. Take a big step forward until both knees are bent at right angles, twisting your torso to the side as you lower. Push off your front foot to return to start position.

▼ Twisting knee raise

Lie flat on the floor with your arms by your sides. Contract your abs to draw your knees in to your chest and raise your torso off the floor, twisting your shoulders to the side as you crunch up.

▼ Leg lower

Lie on your back with your legs straight up in the air. Contract your abs to lower your legs to the floor but stop just before your heels touch the ground then raise them again.

▼ Side crunch

Lie on your side with your knees bent. Contract your side abs to crunch to the side.

▼ Plank

Position yourself so that your body is straight from head to heels with your elbows below your shoulders. Hold that position and don't let your hips sag.

IMPROVE CARDIO ENDURANCE

Get fitter and faster with our six-week 10K training plan

• What is cardio endurance and why do I need to improve it?

When you exercise your heart and lungs – your cardiovascular system – has to work hard to transport blood and oxygen to the working muscles, and the more efficient they are at doing this, the greater your levels of fitness. The higher your level of cardio endurance, the harder and longer you will be able to run, swim or cycle without having to slow down to rest or recover. So training to improve cardio endurance is the best way to get stronger and faster, whatever your sport or discipline.

• What's the best way to improve cardio endurance?

To improve your cardio endurance fitness you need to be pushing your cardiovascular system out of its comfort zone on a regular basis to force your heart, lungs and muscles into growing stronger and more efficient. To do this you need include some tough, heart-pumping, lung-busting sessions into your long-term training programme: interval sessions (alternating between high, moderate and low intensity exercise); threshold sessions (training at as close to your

maximum effort as possible for as long as possible); and hill training (powering up a hill before recovering on the way back down). The following six-week training plan – for a 10K road race – includes all these sessions, in addition to lighter, recovery runs, to improve your cardio endurance for all sports while aiming to set a new 10K personal best in the process.

STRETCHING TRY TO STRETCH EVERY DAY FOR TEN TO 15 MINUTES.

'10K is a great distance to run without having to spend hours and hours training'

• Why do a 10K race?

Whether you are a first-timer or ready for a new fitness challenge, a 10K race is a great distance to challenge yourself without having to spend hours and hours training. A 10K race is ideal for those stepping up from the 5K distance and is the perfect preparation for anyone thinking of doing a half marathon. It's a very popular distance in the UK with races all over the country throughout the year, varying from small races organised by local running clubs all the way up to mass-participation

events that draw some of the world's best athletes.

• What key skills will I need over this distance?

The most important attribute in posting a decent 10K time is having good speed endurance. Unfortunately, this is one of the toughest and most painful things to train for because it requires a lot of training sessions at a pace that is as fast as you can go for a sustainable period of time, such as threshold sessions. As your cardiovascular system and muscles become better through training you will notice a vast improvement in your levels of cardio endurance and consequently see your 10K time plummet.

• How will I know when I'm ready for a 10K race?

The beauty of a 10K race is that you can just give it a go if you are in reasonable fitness. However, if you want to test if you are really ready to post a good time then try running a 5K at your predicted 10K race pace. If you finish this with plenty left in the tank then you are ready to try to set a new personal best.

GET FIT FOR A 10K

Be ready for the starting line in six weeks with this plan

WK	MONDAY	TUESDAY	WEDNESDAY	THURSDAY	FRIDAY	SATURDAY	SUNDAY
1	Rest	**Cross-training** 30min. Focus on general body conditioning.	**Threshold run** 4 x 3min at level 8 with 2min recovery at level 3 after each interval.	Rest	**Cross-training** 30-40min. Focus on general body conditioning.	**Hilly run** Run 25min at level 5, working harder on the climbs.	Run 40min at level 4.
2	Rest	**Cross-training** 1hr. Focus on general body, core and leg exercises.	**Threshold run** 2 x 6min at level 8 with 3min recovery at level 3 after each interval.	Rest	Run 40min at level 5 with 6 x 90sec at level 9. Recover for at least 1min between fast bursts.	Bike ride 1hr.	Run 50min at level 4.
3	Rest	**Cross-training** 1hr. Focus on general body, core and leg exercises.	Run 40min at level 5 with 2 x 8min at level 8. Recover for at least 3min between fast bursts.	Rest	**Threshold run** 5 x 4min at level 8 with 90sec recovery at level 3 after each interval.	Rest	Run 55min at level 4.
4	Rest	**Cross-training** 1hr. Focus on general body, core and leg exercises.	**Threshold run** 2 x 10min at level 8 with 3min recovery at level 3 after each interval.	Rest	Run 40min at level 5 with 6 x 90sec at level 9. Recover for at least 1min between fast bursts.	Rest	Run 1hr at level 4.
5	Rest	**Cross-training** 1hr. Focus on general body, core and leg exercises.	Run 45min at level 5 with middle 15min at level 8.	Rest	**Threshold run** 5 x 3min at level 8 with 90sec recovery at level 3 after each interval.	Rest	Run 40min at level 4.
6	Rest	Rest	**Threshold run** 2 x 5min at level 8 with 2min recovery at level 3 after each interval.	Rest	Rest	10-15min easy jog and light stretching.	**RACE DAY**

TRAINING KEY

Effort levels

1-3   Easy up to a gentle pace
4-5   Able to have a conversation
6-7   Getting out of breath
8-9   Can't talk
10   Flat-out sprint

Threshold session

Run at the maximum pace you can sustain for the length of the session. This kind of run is tough but will push your fitness forwards.

Cross-training

As well as the sessions in the plan, always substitute cross-training for running if you are injured, feeling sore or if it's not safe to run. Add a Pilates or yoga class once or twice a week as well if you have time.

WARM-UP ALWAYS DO A 10-MINUTE WARM-UP BEFORE ANY THRESHOLD SESSION

EAT FOR A BETTER BODY

Good nutrition is half the battle, so understanding the basics of nutrition will give you a head start when it comes to changing your body

1 Watch your calories

Put simply, if you eat fewer calories than you burn off through activity you will lose weight. If you eat more, you'll gain weight. Whether you gain it as fat or muscle depends on what you eat and how you train. As a rule of thumb the average man needs around 2,500 calories a day, but as you'll see in rule five (p50), quality counts more than quantity when it comes to calories.

2 Get the balance right

Nearly all your calories come from a combination of carbohydrates, protein and fats. Carbohydrates provide the glycogen that fuels your workouts, while protein is required to grow new tissue in your body and is therefore of special interest to anyone trying to build muscle. The optimum intake of protein for muscle-gainers is between 1.5g and 2g of protein per kilo of bodyweight, but it doesn't hurt to take in a bit more.

Fat is a nutrient that many people try to avoid altogether, but it can help you absorb vitamins, improve athletic performance and protect joints and tendons against injury. It is though very calorie dense, so you only need about 50-60g a day.

3 Eat the right stuff

The simplest rule when deciding what to eat is: keep it natural. The less processed your food the better. This is especially true of carbohydrates, which provide the energy you need to train hard, but can also alter your blood sugar levels, causing you store fat. Aim to make the majority of your carbs unrefined, unprocessed, low on the glycaemic index and high in fibre. This includes wholegrain bread, wholewheat pasta, oats, beans, fruit and vegetables. These will release energy slowly, ensuring you always have enough stored glycogen in your muscles for a workout.

Protein-rich foods include lean meat, fish, eggs, dairy produce and soya. Lower quality protein can also be found in nuts, seeds and beans. Aim

> 'Eat small meals at intervals of two or three hours, with the aim of having protein with every meal'

to eat a wide variety of protein foods to get the full range of muscle-building amino acids, but be wary of taking in too much saturated fat, such as can be found in poor cuts of red meat and dairy items. Not all fats are bad, as you'll see in rule three on the next page, but try to make most of your fat the monounsaturates and polyunsaturate kind, found in olive oil, nuts,seeds and oily fish. These include omega 3 and omega 6 fatty acids which have been proven to aid strength and aerobic training.

4 Eat at the right times

When you're training hard you want to eat about an hour or two before your workouts, and again immediately afterwards. Your snacks should include both carbs and protein to help restore glycogen levels in your muscles and repair muscle tissue. A perfect post-workout snack might be a bagel with cream cheese, or a tuna and pasta salad.

For the rest of the day, eat small meals at regular intervals of two or three hours, with the aim of having some protein with every meal. This way you keep your glycogen levels topped up and prevent your body from breaking down the proteins that you need for muscle rebuilding.

5 Take on fluids

When you work out you sweat a lot, and you need to need to replace that fluid with water. The trick is to ensure that you hydrate yourself before you get thirsty, not afterwards. Dehydration will impact on your performance in the gym and can affect the way your body stores fat and repairs muscle owing to poor organ function. Take a water bottle with you to the gym and sip from it every few minutes. Over the course of a day you should aim to take in about three litres of water in total. Alcohol, on the other hand, you can do without. It can have a catabolic effect on your muscles, preventing them from developing properly. If you're serious about training, keep pub nights to a minimum.

6 Supplement sparingly

Sports supplements, such as protein powders and energy drinks, aren't an alternative to a good diet. Eating healthily is more important than glugging down shakes, but they do have one advantage: convenience. If you're trying to build muscle can be tough to consume all the calories you need through food alone so supplement can be useful. And exercise can mean you need extra vitamins C and E, so a supplement of these can be handy. But if you do use one be sure to pick a reputable brand.

THE NEW RULES OF FOOD

Eating properly shouldn't take a diploma, so we've simplified everything you need to know into seven simple rules

What you eat is every bit as important to your fitness as what you do in the gym, but every week different fad diets and scare stories hit the news, making it impossible to work out which bits of advice are right. It's easy to justify bad choices – after all, scientists and nutritionists are constantly changing their minds, right? Wrong.

Those in the know agree on what you should be putting in your mouth – and what's more, it's much simpler than you'd expect. Here, we've distilled that collective wisdom into seven rules simple enough to scribble on a postcard. Memorise them, take them shopping or stick them on the fridge – and tuck in.

RULE ONE
GREEN IS GOOD

We're starting with this because it could define how you think about the rest of your diet: there's no such thing as too much veg, especially if you're talking about vegetables grown above ground. Regardless of what else you're eating, your plate should be about half-full of them.

The Food Standards Agency's 'eatwell plate', which has replaced the traditional food pyramid as the government-endorsed illustration of what to eat, suggests that roughly a third of your diet should come from fruit and veg. But it also suggests that another third should be made up of 'bread, rice, potatoes and other starchy foods'. This is not the way to a hard, lean body, because the fundamental problem with starchy carbohydrates is they cause sudden and prolonged rises in blood sugar, which is known to provoke a slew of biochemical imbalances that predispose you to weight gain, type 2 diabetes

and other nasty health problems. If you're going to eat carbohydrate, make sure it's more nutritious carbohydrate with slower sugar release, which is almost every vegetable apart from the potato.

It's also an oversimplification to put fruit and vegetables together, as the FSA plate does. Yes, they're both good for you, but they're radically different nutritionally. If you're getting your five a day from fruit alone, then the fructose will send your blood sugar levels crazy throughout the day.

Remember you'd have to eat half a kilo of asparagus to ingest the same amount of carbs as you get in a single wholemeal pitta bread.

BITE-SIZED SUMMARY Make vegetables the foundation of your diet, along with two pieces of fruit a day. Vary them as much as you can.

RULE TWO
EAT PROTEIN WITH EVERYTHING

Sooner or later, you'll run into someone at the gym, office or all-you-can-eat buffet who raises an eyebrow at the amount of protein you're ingesting. Some may even tell you confidently that it can be bad for your health.

Here's the truth: the only studies that have ever suggested that protein can cause kidney problems were done on people with pre-existing kidney problems. The studies showing that it's harmful to anyone else simply don't exist.

When you eat a high-protein diet, you're generally less hungry, eat less and lose weight as a result. So what's the right amount? Estimates vary from one to four grams per kilo of bodyweight, per day, but most nutritionists agree that two grams is the minimum. As for how

much you can digest at one sitting, a 2009 study from Canada's McMaster University found that increasing protein intake per meal only increased protein synthesis (raised the amount the body could use) up to a dose of roughly 20 grams – though the study focused specifically on egg proteins, so others might behave differently.

So what does this boil down to when you're making your dinner? 'Stick to a two-to-one ratio of vegetables to protein in every meal, by sight.

BITE-SIZED SUMMARY It's almost impossible to eat too much protein, although you could easily not be getting enough. Eat it with every meal.

RULE THREE
DON'T FEAR FAT

Although most of us know that eating some fat is essential to a healthy diet, it's all too easy to make a mental connection between eating fat and *getting* fat, so you end up simply skipping it. Trouble is, that usually means eating something that's worse for you.

One possible issue the FSA has with fat is that it's more calorific (nine per gram, compared to around four for carbohydrates and protein) so if you're worried about your weight one of the keys is to eat foods that are genuinely satisfying because you'll eat less of them, which you'll often do with fat. You also want to avoid spikes in insulin, which is what you're going to get if you're eating carbs instead.

Although some recent studies have suggested that the link between saturated fats and heart

RULE I

GREEN IS GOOD

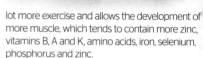

'Only eat food that once grew in or out of the ground, or that once had a face'

disease, may not be as strong as once thought, hydrogenated and trans fats found in many processed foods should still sound alarm bells. Stick instead to naturally occurring fats, whether they're found in red meat, fish, avocado or nuts.

BITE-SIZED SUMMARY Avoided partially hydrogenated fats – especially trans fats. Don't worry too much about the rest.

RULE FOUR
START AS YOU MEAN TO GO ON

You always eat breakfast, of course you do, because you know it's the most important meal of the day and that skipping it slows your metabolism to a crawl. But are you still getting it wrong? You will be if you listen to the FSA's recommendation that you 'base your breakfast on bread or breakfast cereals,' and 'wash it down with some fruit juice'.

Eating a high-carb breakfast will give you low blood-sugar by mid-morning, making you more likely to snack on more high-carb foods, which creates a vicious circle of snacking.

So instead of starting your day on toast or cereal, have something low-carb that's more nutritionally sustainable such as a plain full-fat yoghurt with berries and nuts or scrambled eggs with smoked salmon or ham.

Alternatively, just see off whatever's in the kitchen because last night's leftovers are one of the best (and cheapest) things you can eat, assuming you're eating right in the first place.

BITE-SIZED SUMMARY Think of breakfast like any other meal: you need a blend of protein, fats and fruit or veg. And there's no law stopping you from eating curry.

RULE FIVE
NOT ALL CALORIES ARE EQUAL

The government may believe calories are important enough to be thinking of requiring

restaurants to include their numbers on menus, but the number of calories you're shovelling in or burning off isn't the only thing that matters in weight maintenance.

This is because calories are not a good indication of what a food is like and the effect it's going to have on your metabolic rate. Not convinced? Think of it this way: would you say that a couple of poached eggs are the 'same' as a can of Coke because they contain a similar number of calories? Us neither.

Also, counting calories makes it too easy to justify bad dietary decisions. Ever heard a friend say that they can eat what they want because they'll burn it off at the gym? They couldn't be more wrong. In fact, the more active you are, the better your nutrition needs to be.

Arguably more important than calorie content is your food's glycaemic load (GL), which indicates how much of a blood sugar spike it'll give you – but manufacturers aren't required to put glycaemic load on packaging.

However, if you've stuck with us this far that shouldn't be a problem. Steering clear of starchy food and sugar means you are already avoiding foods with high GL anyway.

You can also slow the absorption rate of high-GL foods, thereby helping prevent blood sugar wobbles, by eating them with more protein-heavy foods, such as chicken or tuna.

BITE-SIZED SUMMARY Think quality, not quantities. Eating nutritious food is much better than sticking rigidly to a 2,500-calorie-a-day limit that comes from toast and crisps.

RULE SIX
FREE RANGE IS KEY

Just in case that bulk-value crate of cage-raised eggs is starting to look tempting, let us take a minute to remind you that favouring organic and free-range meat and fish is better for your body.

For instance, free range chickens have a more varied diet and they obtain a

lot more exercise and allows the development of more muscle, which tends to contain more zinc, vitamins B, A and K, amino acids, iron, selenium, phosphorus and zinc.

Also, farm-raised salmon have been found to contain up to eight times the level of polychlorinated biphenyls, or PCBs, a possible human carcinogen, as their wild brethren, while grass-fed beef tends to have much higher levels of conjugated linoleic acid, thought to help prevent cancer and omega 3s, which are linked to all sorts of health benefits, than the kind fed on grain and beef tallow.

Eating free range feels less like a frivolous luxury if you think of it this way: it's so nutritionally dissimilar to cage-reared that it's basically different food.

BITE-SIZED SUMMARY Eat free-range chickens, grass-fed beef and wild-caught salmon when you can. If you don't know where it's from, chances are the answer isn't good.

RULE SEVEN
EAT REAL FOOD

This is the key. If you do this, you'll end up following all the other rules almost by default.

A simple rule of thumb is to only eat food that once grew in or out of the ground or food that once had a face. Alternatively, simply go caveman and think like a hunter-gatherer. When you're looking at food on the supermarket shelf, ask yourself if that food would have existed 5,000 years ago. If the answer is no, then you probably shouldn't be eating it.

You may find it easier to stick to the outer aisles of the supermarket, which is where all the fresh produce is usually kept, and away from the interior where everything is canned, processed or packed full of preservatives.

Avoid things containing preservatives that you can't spell or ingredients you wouldn't keep in the kitchen. Eat things that will rot eventually, so that you know they're fresh. And eat food you enjoy.

BITE-SIZED SUMMARY Eat food, not products pretending to be food.

RULE 6

FREE RANGE IS KEY

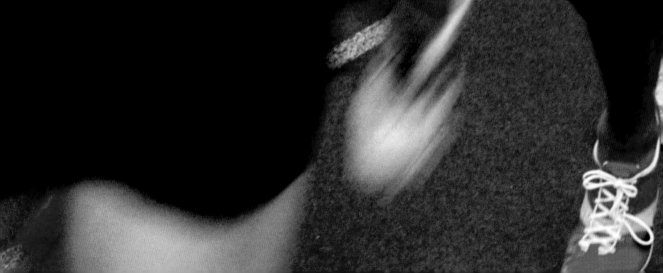

Athletics›

POWER AND GLORY

Build the explosive fitness of a track and field athlete

There are 26 sports and 39 disciplines in the Olympics but athletics takes centre stage. As pure tests of physical ability (fastest man on earth, longest jumper, longest thrower, for example) the events require athletes to give absolutely everything. Well, nearly everything, given that Usain Bolt seems to have won his races before the finish line. But for every other athlete it's an all-out effort.

Ready to explode

The different track and field events might seem like they require different strengths and that's partly true. A sprinter needs more explosive power than a long-distance runner, who needs enormous aerobic capacity. But at the heart of the training programmes for every athlete is strength development. And, more specifically, strength development that allows them to use and control their body as one well-functioning machine. That's why 400m hurdle world champion Dai Greene, does whole body moves, such as the hang snatch (p59), and former world champion triple jumper, Phillips Idowu, does functional exercises such as the single leg decline squat (p63). Follow their training plans and you'll be fitter, faster and stronger than

WORLD'S FASTEST MEN

Here's how the 100m record has tumbled over the decades

Time	Wind	Name	Country	Venue	Date
10.6	n/a	Donald Lippincott	USA	Stockholm	6 Jul 1912
10.4	n/a	Charlie Paddock	USA	Redlands	23 Apr 1921
10.2	1.2	Jesse Owens	USA	Chicago	20 Jun 1936
10.0	0.9	Armin Hary	FRG	Zurich	21 Jun 1960
9.95	0.3	Jim Hines	USA	Mexico City	14 Oct 1968
9.86	1.0	Carl Lewis	USA	Tokyo	25 Aug 1991
9.84	0.7	Donovan Bailey	CAN	Atlanta	27 July 1996
9.79	0.1	Maurice Greene	USA	Athens	16 Jun 1999
9.74	1.7	Asafa Powell	JAM	Rieti	9 Sep 2007
9.58	0.9	Usain Bolt	JAM	Berlin	16 Aug 2009

TAKE A RUNNING JUMP

A combination of speed, endurance and seriously powerful calves is the key to 400m hurdling success. World champion Dai Greene explains how he gets in winning shape

Dai Greene
Born 11th April 1986
Height 1.86m
Weight 70kg
From Felinfoel
ACHIEVEMENTS
● 2011 Gold medallist, world championships
● 2010 Gold medallist, European championships

PART 1
Foot and calf stability

A vital part of hurdling is landing without a wobble. 'The biggest force applied is at the point of contact and people often forget that,' says Greene. 'Everyone builds up their glutes and hamstrings, but strengthening your feet to take the impact is essential.'

1 Round the clock
Sets **2**
Reps **until fatigue**

● Stand on one foot and use the other one to touch the numbers on an imaginary clock face around you.
● As you warm-up, touch further away and lower your centre of gravity to make the exercise harder.

GREENE SAYS 'Don't make this easy on yourself – go for the difficult "numbers" and keep going until you're tired.'

2 Toe tap
Sets **3**
Reps **until fatigue**

● Bounce up and down on your toes, making sure you just move vertically without letting your feet move forwards. If the move feels easy, you're doing it wrong.
● Build up to holding a weight plate above your head, keeping your back straight to emphasise your posture.

GREENE SAYS 'This isn't as easy as it looks. It took me six weeks of doing this every day to start doing it with a weight. Your feet shouldn't be going forwards or backwards, just up and down.'

3 Band stability swing
Sets **3**
Reps **until fatigue**

● With a resistance band around one ankle and the other end secured, move your foot laterally, then turn 90˚ and repeat.
● Do the move in all four ranges of motion before changing legs.

GREENE SAYS 'Lots of my team-mates will say, "that's easy," but then they'll find they can't do this at all.'

PART 2
Strength and power

'At the start of the training season we'll do 45-minute runs, and more aerobic work where we don't push the heart rate up too much,' says Greene. 'Around January we'll do track reps, going for 300-400m reps – a lot, maybe as many as ten. It's similar with gym work: I'll start with high reps, then build up to lower reps with more weight. It's to get the volume in so I'm strong enough to do the short, sharp work.'

1 Hip flexor cable pull
Sets **2**
Reps **10 each side**

● Strap a cable attachment around your ankle and bring your leg up and to the side, then forwards, before lowering it.
● Your leg should mimic the movement the trailing leg makes when it clears a hurdle.

GREENE SAYS 'This isolates the muscles around the hips. It's easy to recover from.'

2 Single-leg glute/ham bridge
Sets **3** Reps **10 each side**

● Keep one foot on the floor close to your glutes and the other in the air, holding a weight plate on your stomach.
● Push up until your knees and shoulders are in a straight line. Try to be explosive on the upward movement.

GREENE SAYS 'I'll usually do around 70kg on this but I've gone as high as 90kg. This really gets your glutes firing. Don't cheat by curving your spine.'

4 Single-leg step-up
Sets **2** Reps **8 each side**

● Holding a barbell across your shoulders – or a pair of dumb-bells if you're less confident – step up on to a box and raise your trailing leg until it's at a right angle to your body.
● Stay upright and repeat the move on both sides.

GREENE SAYS 'I'll often superset this with a hang snatch.'

3 Hang snatch
Sets **3** Reps **5**

● Start the move holding the bar just below your knees, with a wide 'snatch' grip, roughly double-shoulder width.
● Explode upwards, then duck under the bar to 'catch' it with straight arms and bent legs. Stand up straight to finish the move.

GREENE SAYS 'As an athlete, the only time my legs are close to 90° is when I'm in the blocks. When I need to produce power, they're closer to 120°, which is the starting position for the hang snatch.'

5 Depth box jump
Sets **3** Reps **5**

● Jump off a small box or step roughly 10cm off the ground.
● As you hit the ground, explode upwards to jump on to a higher step.

GREENE SAYS 'I'm not going off a huge depth here. The whole point is that I need to generate explosive power after I've just come down from a hurdle, and my foot and ankle stability needs to be top-notch. It's a power exercise but doubles up as an ankle stiffness exercise.'

POWER OF THREE

Build explosive power with triple jumper
Phillips Idowu's drills and strength moves

Phillips Idowu

Born 30th December 1978
Height 1.92m
Weight 87kg
ACHIEVEMENTS
- 2011 Silver medallist, world championships
- 2010 Gold medallist, European championships
- 2009 Gold medallist, world championships
- 2008 Silver medallist, Beijing Olympics
- 2007 Gold medallist, European indoor championships

PART 1 Running and jumping stability

1 Front hurdle step-over
Sets **3** Reps **5 each side**

- Stand facing a series of hurdles.
- Lift one knee and send your foot over the hurdle, keeping your toes up and your back leg straight.
- Land on the ball of your foot, then lift your back leg so it goes out to the side and over the hurdle.
- Plant the trailing foot alongside your leading foot.
- Keep your upper body as still as possible.

IDOWU SAYS 'This drill improves your hip mobility to increases your range of movement, helping you jump further.'

2 Resistance band twist
Sets **3**
Reps **6 each side**

- Start with your feet shoulder-width apart.
- Secure the band at waist height and hold it to one side with your arms extended.
- Rotate your torso, keeping your arms straight.
- Increase the resistance as you get stronger.

IDOWU SAYS 'When you jump you need to stabilise your back muscles quickly. This move is particularly good for activating your back and core muscles.'

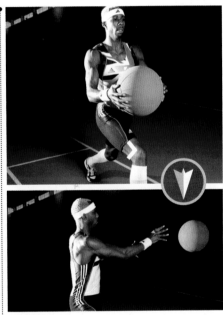

3 Static lunge medicine ball throw
Sets **3** Reps **5 each side**

- Start with your front foot flat on the ground and your knee bent at 90°.
- Keep the ball of your back foot on the floor and your back leg fairly straight.
- Hold the medicine ball out in front of you.
- Rotate your hips and torso away from your front leg and throw the ball at a wall or to your partner.

IDOWU SAYS 'Doing the throw in a lunge position gives you strength in an unstable stance.'

PART 2 Running and jumping power

1 Hang snatch
Sets **3** Rep **8**

- Start by holding the bar at your thighs with your knees bent.
- Lift the bar powerfully, keeping a natural arch in your back and duck under the bar to 'catch' it with straight arms before standing up straight.

IDOWU SAYS 'This uses less momentum than lifting from the ground, so you have to generate more force.'

2 Cable knee raise
Sets **3** Reps **5** **each side**

- Secure a cable around your ankle and hold it off the ground behind your standing leg with your toes up.
- Keeping your upper body still, raise your knee as high as possible.
- Control the working leg back to the start without letting it touch the ground.

IDOWU SAYS 'Producing power going forward is vital in triple jumping. Start off doing this move slowly and progress by increasing the speed.'

3 Single leg decline squat
Sets **3** Reps **6** each side

● Stand with a barbell on your shoulders with one foot on a declining surface and the other off the floor.
● Keeping your knee in line with your foot, sink down as low as you can go without wobbling or rounding your shoulders.
● Start with a shallow decline and build up as you get stronger.

IDOWU SAYS 'This move really strengthens the stabilisers around your knee, which is important because of the forces you absorb when jumping.'

4 Dumb-bell roll-out
Sets **3** Reps **8**

● Start with your back straight and hold the dumb-bells beneath your shoulders.
● Keeping your back and arms straight, roll the dumb-bells out as far as you can without breaking form.
● Roll one of the dumb-bells in to your chest, then roll it back out and repeat on the other side to complete one rep.

IDOWU SAYS 'This move is great for developing core stability. Using dumb-bells rather than a bar is a progression because it forces you to stabilise yourself more.'

OFF TO A FLYER

British long jump record holder Chris Tomlinson on how to make a giant leap

STEP 1

STEP 2

STEP 3

STEP 1 'I take four or five walk-in strides, then I have roughly a 46m run-up, where I'm building up speed, really digging in with my strides.'

STEP 2 'The attack is four or five strides going into the board, setting up the take-off. This is where lifts, such as the power clean come into play.'

STEP 4

STEP 5

STEP 3 'I've already built up most of my speed on the run, so the take-off is about keeping over the front of the board and driving as high as I can.'

STEP 4 'The "hang" is what the snatch builds strength for. Other athletes use a hitch-kick, but I prefer to use a style where as little can go wrong as possible in the jump.'

STEP 5 'This is what the leg raise builds towards – you're making an aerodynamic shape and keeping your weight forward for landing.'

Chris Tomlinson

Born 15th Sept 1981
Height 1.98m
Weight 85kg
ACHIEVEMENTS
● 2011 British record holder (8.35m)
● 2010 Bronze medallist European championships

Lawrence Okoye

Born 6th October 1991
Height 1.96m
Weight 127kg
ACHIEVEMENTS
- 2011 British record holder (67.63m)
- 2011 Gold medallist, European under-23 championships
- 2010 6th place, junior world championships
- 2010 Gold medallist, UK under-20 championships

THROW YOUR WEIGHT

British discus record holder Lawrence Okoye demonstrates the drills that build raw power

Workout for discus strength and agility

2 Underarm
Sets **1** Reps **6**

- Face the opposite way from the overheads and this time use your hips to accelerate yourself up and forwards.
- Drive from your heels all the way through to the release.

OKOYE SAYS 'Underarms are more quad-based but again it helps develop explosive power in the hips and legs. All the power should be coming from the lower body to mimic the discus throw.'

1 Overhead
Sets **1** Reps **10**

- Stand on a platform holding a medicine ball, or 7.26kg rubber shot put, with straight arms.
- Squat down and drive your hips forwards and your whole body up and back off the floor to launch the weight behind you.

OKOYE SAYS 'Overheads are an explosive move upwards, involving mainly your hips and lower back, and powerful hips are vital to get distance in your discus throw.'

3 Standing jump
Sets **1** Reps **10**

- Use your arms to generate momentum and drive forwards with your hips.
- As a variation perform three standing jumps one after the other as a single rep, maintaining energy and momentum.

OKOYE SAYS 'It's important to channel your energy through your whole body and this will transfer the motion from my arms all the way through to my leg drive. My PB is 3.31m.'

Workout for discus strength and agility

4 Power clean
Sets **5** Reps **3-5**

- Hold a bar level with your thighs with hands shoulder-width apart.
- Explode upwards with your hips bringing the bar up to shoulder height and then back down. Your arms should do as little of the work as possible.

OKOYE SAYS 'I do normal cleans, but this technique, where you don't "catch" the bar at the top, means I can go heavier with the weight, which emphasises the power I can generate from my hips. I usually hit around 140kg for three.'

5 Power snatch
Sets **5** Reps **3-5**

- Hold a bar with hands double shoulder-width apart.
- Drive your hips forward and accelerate the bar upwards to around head height before lowering.

OKOYE SAYS 'I use exactly the same principle when performing the snatch as with the clean. It's all about intensity and dynamic movement so keep the reps low but weight high. I'll normally reach around 100kg for three.'

Anatomy of a discus throw

Lawrence Okoye explains how his training produces a 67m-plus discus throw

'Stand tall at the back of the circle with hips forwards and knees bent slightly. Relax and twist from side to side to wind up.'

'Pivot on the ball of your left foot, getting your bodyweight outside the circle with a long sweep of your right leg.'

'Turning back into the circle, drive hard off your left leg jumping towards the front. This is where the overheads, underarms and standing jump work come in.'

6 Barbell twist
Sets **3** Reps **10-15**

● Stand holding a barbell across your shoulders.
● Bracing your core twist from side to side slowly, keeping your head looking forwards.

OKOYE SAYS 'This helps mirror the rotation required for the discus. It is all about getting the midsection and obliques strong because they take a battering when you throw.'

7 Barbell side bend
Sets **3** Reps **5 each side**

● Hold an empty bar with hands twice shoulder-width apart and straight arms.
● Contracting your core, slowly bend to one side. Alternate each side.

OKOYE SAYS 'Make sure it's a slow, controlled movement. Contract your obliques as hard as possible to work the core. I normally use an empty 20kg barbell.'

'Sweep your right leg back in, aiming to land in the circle's middle, and put your left foot down at the front quickly. Keep your upper body as "wrapped" as possible.'

'There are two ways of throwing at this point: feet down or reverse. Reversers leave the ground when they deliver and their right foot replaces the left. I throw feet down.'

'To throw feet down turn your right foot, knee and hip inwards so your right leg hits your left but both stay on the floor. This makes the delivery more like a punch.'

'Good balance, and ensuring you put the generated force through the discus, will keep you within the circle so you don't foul.'

LONDON CALLING

Heptathlete Jessica Ennis is Britain's big Olympic gold medal hope. The Sheffield-based athlete tells us how she trains and what she thinks her chances are for 2012

As the run-up to the London Olympics reaches its final stretch, one athlete has firmly emerged as the face of 2012.

Despite disappointment at last summer's world championships, the Sheffield born heptathlete, Jessica Ennis, has been so consistently impressive over the past two years that she represents our best hope of winning a track and field gold medal.

'It definitely adds more pressure,' says the 25-year-old when asked about being the 2012 poster girl. 'I think all the British athletes are going to have more pressure on them because it's a home Olympics. And once you start winning medals people expect you to do it all the time.' Victory isn't a formality because Ennis faces stiff competition from Russian and Ukrainian challengers. A poor performance in the javelin, meant she missed out on gold to her Russian rival Tatyana Chernova at the world championships. But she still produced personal bests in the long jump, the shot and the 800m, and if her good form continues her chances of finding herself the top of the podium in London are looking good.

The Olympics are only months away. What shape do you feel you're in?
I'm probably in the best running shape I've ever been in – last season I ran PBs in the 200m and the 800m. That shows I'm in good shape but I still feel like I need to sharpen up a bit.

What are you working on?
Everything. Well, it's the second day [long jump, javelin and 800m] that I want to improve. You're

---

Jessica Ennis

Born 28th Jan 1986
Height 1.65m
Weight 57kg
ACHIEVEMENTS
- 2011 Silver medallist, world championships
- 2010 Gold medallist, European championships
- 2010 Gold medallist, world indoor championships, pentathlon

---

tired and you wake up a bit stiff and sore on the second day but the long jump is something that we've worked on for a while. And the javelin as well.

How happy are you with your long jump?
I haven't achieved what I should have in that event. My speed is there and my jumping in the high jump is there, but it hasn't yet translated into my long jump. I jumped 6.51m [her best non wind-assisted jump] in New York in 2010 and again at Daegu, which was a big breakthrough.

What are your best and worst training sessions?
I enjoy hurdling but I hate the 800m training. We do one session a week of 200m intervals and it's horrendous but it helps so much. At the end of it I feel like dying. Normally I'm just lying on the track.

What techniques do you use to get through difficult sessions?
Once you get into the routine of doing them, you feel OK. Your body may be in pieces but you feel really good because you know that session is in the tank for the summer. That keeps you motivated and driving forwards.

Are you always tired?
Pretty much. The hardest training is through the winter – a lot of volume, a lot of sessions, a lot of heavy weights and conditioning circuits. The first couple of weeks, your body is in pieces. Those few months through the winter, everything is pretty difficult. But once you come out the other side, it gets a little bit easier, you sharpen up and you really feel the benefit of that volume of training.

What's your advice for running faster?
We do short sprints, which is good for getting the legs turning over quickly. We do a lot of explosive stuff in the gym. We do the Olympic lifts, which is good for leg speed and strength.

What lifts do you do?
The Olympic lifts, full cleans, hang cleans, hang snatch, bench press, hamstring exercises, core exercises. Working every muscle, basically.

What weight do you lift?
I can't give that away! Sets and reps vary throughout the year. I'm currently doing four sets of three at 85-90 per cent of my maximum.

If you could get rid of one event and bring in a new one, what would you pick?
I would definitely get rid of the 800m because it's too far and too painful. What would I put in? Something nice and short like the 100m. It would be great if that was the final event.

What sports will you be watching in 2012?
Lots of athletics – the 100m final should be amazing – and things like diving and gymnastics. A lot of the British boxers are based in Sheffield so I'd like to see some of the boxing.

'After an 800m session I feel like dying. I'm just lying on the track'

POWERADE

Rowing ›

KINGS OF THE WATER

Follow in the footsteps of Britain's greatest Olympian

There will be pressure on the British athletes to deliver medals at the 2012 games and that's because Britain traditionally does well in boats. After athletics, rowing has been our most successful Olympic sport, with 24 gold, 20 silver and 10 bronze medals. It has also produced our greatest ever Olympian, Sir Steve Redgrave, who won five gold medals and a bronze during a career that spanned five Olympic games.

Pure fitness

When you think of rowing races at the Olympics, the images that stick in your mind are often of the athletes bent double and breathing heavily at the end of the race. Few sportsmen can match the effort levels that rowers produce and that's something acknowledged by Redgrave. 'It's a sheer fitness sport,' he says. 'It doesn't matter how talented you are, if you haven't done the training you won't win the races.' That's why the workouts in this chapter are arguably the toughest in the entire book. Olympic gold medal winner Andy Hodge takes us through the big power moves he does to build explosive strength. Then his team-mate, and fellow gold medal winner, Peter Reed demonstrates a circuit that will challenge even the fittest of aspiring Olympians.

ROWING JARGON BUSTER

Coxswain The coxswain, or 'cox', sits at the stern and is responsible for steering the boat and directing the crew.
Lightweight In women's lightweight events, no rower may weigh more than 59kg, with an average weight per crew member not exceeding 57kg. For men, the single-rower maximum is 72.5kg, and the maximum crew member average shall not exceed 70kg.
Scull To row with two oars, one in each hand.
Sweep To row with one oar.

These are the rowers and oars involved in each discipline

Coxless pairs* (CoxLess - one oar each)
Coxless fours (CL - one oar each)
Eights (with cox – only one with coxswain – one oar each)
Lightweight coxless four* (CL - one oar each)
Single sculls (CL – two oars, one in each hand)
Lightweight double sculls
(CL – two oars, one in each hand)
Double sculls (CL – two oars, one in each hand)
Quadruple sculls without coxswain
(CL – two oars, one in each hand)
*No women's event

POWER BOAT

Discover how British rower Andrew Hodge delivers maximum power with every stroke

PART 1
Rowing power

'The key component of a good rowing stroke is delivering maximum dynamic power throughout the body,' says Hodge. 'So we'll do a lot of full-body moves that emphasise that. We also do a lot of unilateral movements. When we drive, we drive through both hips at a slightly different angle, and with the amount of strokes we do a day you can get into some real problems because of imbalances in the amount each muscle works. So it's important to balance that out in training. We'll do a lot of pushing movements for the same reason – if you work just your pulling muscles you'll end up imbalanced and injured.'

1 Split squat
Sets 3
Reps 5 each side

● With a barbell on your back take a big step forwards, then bend your front knee until your back knee brushes the floor.
● Don't return to upright between reps.

HODGE SAYS 'Don't drop your tail leg to the floor to make the move easier. You want your back in an upright, strong position.'

2 Power clean
Sets 5   Reps 3

● Start with feet shoulder-width apart and grip the bar just outside your knees. Drive up and rise up on to your toes, pulling the bar upwards, then drop underneath and catch it on top of your chest.
● As with a rowing stroke, most of the drive should come from your legs – you shouldn't really feel this move in your arms.

HODGE SAYS 'You want to engage your posterior chain, so stay on your heels through the drive and accelerate as you go up. As soon as your hands pass your knees, accelerate the bar up so you can drop under and catch it.'

3 Bent-over row
Sets 3 Reps 6

● Lean forward at the hips and hold a bar at roughly knee height, keeping your back straight and neck in line with your spine. Brace your core and retract your shoulder blades as you pull the bar up to your sternum.

HODGE SAYS 'The pull is the last part of the drive phase. It doesn't contribute so much to the speed of the boat, but if you lose control of the oar then you've lost control of the boat. You want your upper body to be strong enough to handle what your legs can deliver.'

4 Dumb-bell bench press
Sets 3 Reps 6

● Lie on a bench, your head and shoulders supported, holding a pair of dumb-bells at chest level.
● Your core should be braced and your feet flat on the floor.
● Press the weights straight up and lower under control.
● Don't arch your back.

HODGE SAYS 'The idea of the bench press is to keep your body balanced. Your press has to be as strong as your pull, or you'll end up with weak links.'

PART 2
Core strength

'A huge amount of rowing is about holding a strong core,' says Hodge. 'So the exercises we do are about exposing the little muscles and engaging everything. A lot of it is neural, where you're trying to set up good working patterns. You don't want to just be good at rowing, you want to be good at a lot of things that contribute to good habits. Getting used to keeping a tight core is a big part of that.'

1 Lighthouse
Sets **3** Reps **8**

● This is a one-legged version of the very tough dragon flag. Bend one leg, then engage your core and raise your legs and hips into the air, aiming to maintain a straight line. Keep your body shape as you lower down under control.

HODGE SAYS 'The whole point of this is that you're trying to keep a good shape. Try to work to a scheme of six seconds per rep.'

2 Barbell rollout
Sets **3** Reps **8**

● Get a barbell with big plates on either side. Kneel and hold the bar with your hands shoulder-width apart, then roll it forwards. If you can touch your chin to the ground, great, otherwise come back up when your hips start to sag.

HODGE SAYS 'This'll take you through the full range of motion you'll go through during a rowing stroke and force you to keep tight all the time.'

3 Resisted side plank
Sets **3**
Reps **5 each side**

● You'll need a training partner for this one. Get in a side plank with your forearm and bottom foot touching the floor, and get your partner to apply steady pressure downwards on your hip. Aim for an amount of pressure that will let you resist for around five seconds each rep.

HODGE SAYS 'This is another move that develops the kind of unilateral core strength you need in the boat.'

Peter Reed

Born 27th July 1981
Height 1.98m
Weight 102kg
ACHIEVEMENTS
● 2011, 2010,
2009 Silver medallist,
coxless pair,
world rowing
championships
● 2008 Gold medallist,
coxless four, Olympics

GOLD STANDARD

Develop impressive strength
endurance with two killer workouts
from top British rower Peter Reed

PART 1 Workout for rowing strength

1 Bench pull
Sets **4** Reps **5**

● Lie on a high bench
with your feet hanging
off the end and your arms
hanging straight down.
● Grab a barbell and pull
it up to the bench,
squeezing your shoulder
blades together at the
top of the move.
REED SAYS 'This is a
great exercise for
strengthening the muscles
that are used at the end of
the row. It's as if this move
was built for rowing.'

4 Bench press
Sets **4** Reps **5**

● Start with your feet on
the bench, your spine
neutral, and hold the bar
above your chest with your
shoulder blades retracted.
● Lower the bar slowly to
your chest and push back
up powerfully.

REED SAYS 'Resting your
feet on the bench puts
your back in a neutral
position and forces you
to engage your core to
stabilise your spine.'

2 Power clean
Sets **4** Reps **5**

● Start with the bar on the floor and grip it just outside your shins.
● Lift the bar powerfully, keeping your elbows high and rising up onto your toes.
● Bend your knees to duck under the bar and catch it on top of your chest.

● Stand up straight and reset the bar before repeating the move.

REED SAYS 'This is a dynamic move that works your whole body. It's the exact movement of a rowing stroke – the way you use your hips and back and then coordination to bring in your arms.'

3 Box squat
Sets **4** Reps **5**

● Rest the bar on the back of your shoulders then lower until you are sitting on the box.
● Pause for one second, keeping your elbows back and your back neutral.
● Push back up through your heels to return to the start.

REED SAYS 'Using a box takes the pressure off during the weakest part of the move, which can be useful for building your confidence and eventually building your range of movement.'

5 Leg press
Sets **4** Reps **8**

● Hold the grips at the side and keep your back pressed against the support.
● Lower the weight until your knees are bent at 90˚ (or further if you have strong quads and stable knees).
● Push through your heels to return to the start.

REED SAYS 'In this move you isolate your leg muscles without taking the load with your back. It's important to include exercises that isolate muscles and also ones that improve your coordination.'

6 Seated row
Sets **4** Reps **5**

● Start with your back straight and your shoulder blades retracted.
● Pull the handle in to your sternum and squeeze your shoulder blades together at the top of the move.
● Return to the start and keep upper-body movement to a minimum throughout the move.

REED SAYS 'The bench pull isolates your arms whereas this coordinates your back and your arms, and is identical to the second half of the rowing stroke.'

PART 2 Circuit for rowing endurance

1 Weighted step-up
Reps 20 each side

● Hold a weight plate to your chest and push up through your whole foot, not just your toes.

2 Pull-up
Reps 10

● Using an overhand grip, hang straight down without swinging, then pull up until your chin is over the bar.

5 Dumb-bell row
Reps 40 each side

● Let the weight hang down below your shoulder then pull it up to your chest, keeping your back flat and your body still.

6 Side plank
Time 60sec

● Hold your body in a straight line from head to heels with your elbow beneath your shoulder. Swap sides each circuit.

3 Feet-up Russian twist
Reps 20

● Holding a weight plate, keep your back straight, knees bent and feet off the floor, then twist your torso from side to side.

4 Squat jump
Reps 40

● Hold a weight plate across your chest, sink into a squat and then push up explosively to jump off the ground.

7 Front squat
Reps 20

● Rest the bar on the front of your shoulders with your elbows pointing forwards. Sink into a squat then push back up through your heels.

8 Cross cable pull on gym ball
Reps 30

● Start with your arms straight and crossed, then pull the cables back until your fists are at your chest.

THE PERFECT STROKE

Hodge explains how to fine-tune your rowing form

'There are six key points to hit in a rowing stroke,' says Hodge. 'The stroke goes legs, body, arms; the recovery is arms, body, legs. You want a strong position throughout each stroke – sit up, keep your shoulders relaxed and don't open up your body too much.'

1 Catch 'This is the start of your pull. Reach forward with your knees bent and arms extended, leaning slightly forward with your head high.'

2 Drive 'The idea here is that you're putting power into the handle through your legs. Straighten your legs and push through your back.'

3 Finish 'You want to finish the stroke as strongly as you can. Leaning back too much doesn't really give you any extra pull. Aim for a bit less than a 45° angle, pulling the handle in to your abs.'

4 Recovery 'Begin your recovery by letting your hands move out first, then bodyrocking forwards before bending your legs. This brings you back to the catch.'

ROWING SESSIONS

How to build technique and improve your speed

Endurance

"**To get started, an absolute beginner should try something along the lines of three five-minute bursts at medium resistance,** looking for a rate of around 25 or 26 strokes per minute. Try to keep on the rower for longer with good technique rather than blasting away."

Power

'**Another option is to go for ten sets of ten power strokes.** You set a strokes-per-minute rate – around 20 – and try to do the biggest strokes you can.'

Aquatics

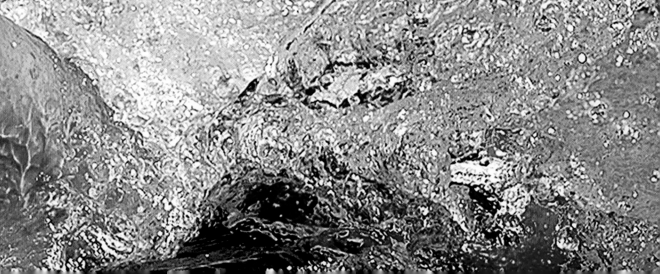

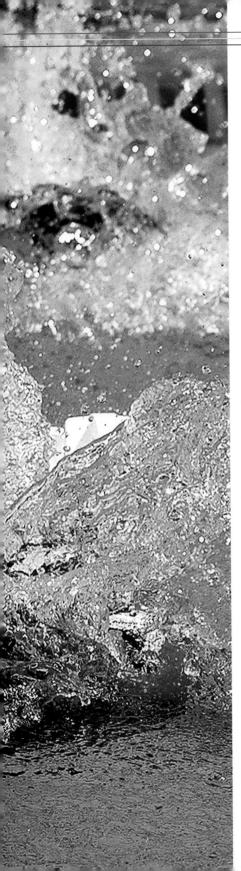

SWIM FOR FITNESS

Train to build a six-pack and a V-shaped torso

The swimming pool seems to overflow with Olympic legends. In 1972 American swimmer Mark Spitz won seven gold medals in Munich. In 2008 another American, Michael Phelps, went one better and bagged eight. No British swimmer is likely to match that haul but backstroke specialist Liam Tancock is hoping to get on the podium.

Take the power back

Swimmers are usually easy to spot. They have board shoulders and almost superhero-like V-shaped torsos. Britain's best swimmer, Liam Tancock, does a lot of back work, including pure strength moves, such as prone pulls, and explosive power exercises, such as medicine ball throws. His strong core, which he needs to stay flat in the water, means he sports a rippling six pack.

The other athlete in this section, the diver Peter Waterfield, goes into rather than through the water but has an equally lean and muscular look. Waterfield brought back silver from Athens in the 10m synchronised dive, and in London is likely to partner Tom Daley.

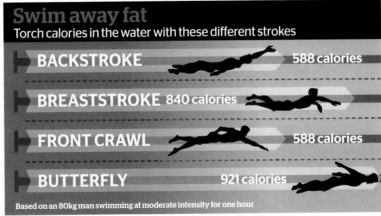

Swim away fat
Torch calories in the water with these different strokes

BACKSTROKE	588 calories
BREASTSTROKE	840 calories
FRONT CRAWL	588 calories
BUTTERFLY	921 calories

Based on an 80kg man swimming at moderate intensity for one hour

WATER POWER

Follow backstroke world champion
Liam Tancock's routine to build
explosive power and core strength

Liam Tancock

Born 7th May 1985
Height 1.83m
Weight 81kg
ACHIEVEMENTS
● 2011, 2009 Gold
medallist, 50m
backstroke world
championships
● 2010 Gold medallist,
50m backstroke
Commonwealth Games
● 2008 Gold medallist,
100m backstroke world
short course
championships

Workout for swimming strength

1a Internal shoulder rotation
Sets **2** Reps **12** each side

- Secure a stretch band around a pole and position your arm so your elbow is tucked in to your chest and your forearm is horizontal.
- Move your forearm in a horizontal arc to bring it in to your chest without letting your elbow leave your side.

1b External shoulder rotation
Sets **2** Reps **12** each side

- Position your arm, as above, but this time with your forearm horizontal across your chest.
- Move your forearm as above to take it away from your chest.

TANCOCK SAYS 'We do a lot of shoulder rotations when we're swimming so these two moves help strengthen the joint and protect it from injury.'

2 Pull-up
Sets **4** Reps **6-8 each side**

- Using an overhand grip, hang straight down without swinging.
- Pull yourself up until your chin is over the bar then lower under control without swinging.

TANCOCK SAYS 'Sprinting involves powerful movements so your back has to be strong. This builds strength and flexibility because you work through a full range of movement.'

Workout for swimming strength

3 Squat
Sets **4** Reps **6-8**

- Start with a barbell resting on your shoulders.
- Keeping your back flat, sink down with your knees over your toes until your thighs are parallel with the floor.

TANCOCK SAYS 'Core strength is vital for swimming and this forces you to engage your core. I also do lightweight squat jumps to build power.'

4 Prone bar pull
Sets **4** Reps **6-8**

- Lie on a high bench and hold a barbell with your arms straight and directly beneath your shoulders.
- Pull the bar up to your chest, then lower slowly to the start.

TANCOCK SAYS 'Lying on a high bench allows you to use your full range of motion, which helps you to stretch on a stroke and increase your efficiency.'

5 Medicine ball explosion
Sets **4** Reps **4**

- Start in a squat position with the medicine ball between your legs.
- Explode upwards, rising onto your toes as you throw the ball up and behind you.

TANCOCK SAYS 'This move helps develop your start. Adding weight with the medicine ball gives you a burst of power.'

6 Barbell rotation
Sets 2 Reps 8 each side

● Sit with a barbell on your shoulders.
● Rotate your torso, still looking straight ahead. Rotate around to the other side, keeping your head facing forwards.

TANCOCK SAYS 'Momentum lets you rotate further. The more rotation you get each stroke, the longer the stroke.'

7 Reverse crunch
Sets 3 Reps 5

● Hold on to a secure anchor with your hands behind your head.
● Use your abs to lift your legs off the floor. Get your body as vertical as you can, keeping it as straight as possible.

TANCOCK SAYS 'I always think of this as a tough, *Rocky*-style move. It teaches you to be strong when your body is in a straight position.'

8 Streamline hold
Sets 3 Time up to 40sec

● Lie on a bench with your upper body over the end and a training partner holding your ankles.
● Get into a 'streamline' position, in which your body is straight from head to heels and your arms are straight with one hand on top of the other.

TANCOCK SAYS 'This move really targets your inner core and lower back. It teaches you to maintain an efficient position in the water.'

BACK TO BASICS

Follow Tancock's tips for getting your backstroke off to a flying start

STEP 1 **Start with your hands on the holds,** your feet shoulder-width apart and your body in a tucked position.

STEP 2 **As you let go, push through the balls of your feet.** Begin to straighten your legs, keeping them together and your toes pointing away from you.

STEP 3 **Push up and back to get an arch in your back** and throw your arms behind your head with one hand on top of the other.

STEP 4 **It's important to lift your hips so you can gain height,** which will give you better entry into the water.

STEP 5 **Try to reduce drag** by entering the water in the smallest area possible.

STEP 6 **The faster you enter the water,** the more momentum you will carry into the underwater phase.

STEP 7 **Go about one metre deep into the water and aim to streamline** (with your body straight and your arms not moving) for up to 15 metres.

GET A DIVER'S BODY

Combining gymnastic strength with a daredevil's approach to self-preservation has given champion diver Peter Waterfield a rock-hard body. Here's how he prepares for competition

Peter Waterfield

Born 12th March 1981
Height 1.68m
Weight 57kg
ACHIEVEMENTS
● 2011, 2010 Gold medallist, national cup, 10m platform
● 2004 Silver medallist, Olympic games, 10m synchronised
● 2002 Gold medallist, Commonwealth games, 10m platform

PART 1
Leg strength

To get big competition scores, divers need to do something elaborate. The more time they have in the air, the better their chances of impressing the judges. That's where leg strength comes in. 'You need to jump as high as you can off the 10m platform because you've got to fit in up to 4.5 somersaults, so you need explosive leg strength to get that height,' says Waterfield.

1 Squat
Sets 5
Reps 6

● Rest the barbell on the back of your shoulders with your core braced.
● Keeping a natural arch in your back and making sure your knees stay in line with your toes, lower until your thighs are parallel to the floor.
● Push back up through your heels to return to the start.

WATERFIELD SAYS
'We do squats at varying speeds. Going down slowly teaches you to control the movement, but exploding up teaches your legs to push off the platform powerfully.'

2 Single-leg step-up
Sets 2 Reps 10
each side

● Plant one foot on a thigh-high platform and push through that foot to straighten your leg. Don't use your standing leg to aid the movement.

WATERFIELD SAYS
'This develops good knee stability across a good range of motion. I do it with bodyweight and then on a slightly lower platform while holding dumb-bells.'

3 Single-leg Romanian deadlift
Sets 5 Reps 5
each side

● Stand holding a barbell across your thighs and lift one foot off the floor.
● Bend at the hips and send the bar down your shin until you feel a strong stretch in your hamstrings, then return to the start.

WATERFIELD SAYS
'It's very important that my hamstrings and glutes fire to get height off the board and this move targets them effectively.'

PART 2
Core stability

'We get into lots of different shapes during our dives, such as tucks, pikes and straight positions so you need a strong core to hold them,' says Waterfield. 'If you're not in control of the dive, you'll lose points. You also hit the water at 40mph [64km/h] so you need your midsection to be strong to hit the water in the right way. And while you're in the air you're spinning so fast that you have to resist the G-force acting on your body.'

1 Side plank
Sets 2
Time 30sec each side

● Position your elbow below your shoulder, then raise your hips so your body is in a straight line from head to heels.
● Aim to hold that position for 30 seconds.

WATERFIELD SAYS
'Static holds help you get better at holding a straight body position. This is also a very good move for strengthening your obliques and glutes.'

2 Tuck kickback
Sets 3 Reps 10

● Start with your calves on a gym ball and your back flat on the floor and hands on your chest.
● Raise your backside off the ground until your body is straight.
● Keeping your upper body still, bring the ball in towards your backside by bending your knees.
● Without letting your hips drop, straighten your legs.

WATERFIELD SAYS 'This develops both core control and technique because it mimics the movement going from a tuck position to a straight body position.'

3 Gym ball pike
Sets 2 Reps 10

● Rest your shins on a gym ball and plant your hands on the floor below your shoulders, arms straight.
● Contract your abs to roll your shins over the ball and simultaneously raise your backside into the air so your body forms an inverted V.

WATERFIELD SAYS 'You have to start one of the dives in a handstand position. Once you're in the pike position of this exercise you can start to move into the handstand position.'

4 Hanging medicine ball pike
Sets 2 Reps 10

● Hang from a bar with your arms straight and a 2-3kg medicine ball between your feet.
● Contract your abs to raise your legs up to the bar.

WATERFIELD SAYS 'This is a good abs and hip flexor exercise that goes through a full range of motion. If you can't do it, start by doing V-sits, then hanging leg raises and then hanging pikes without the medicine ball.'

Combat sports

FIGHTING FIT

Do these boxing and judo drills to develop knockout fitness

Fighting's been a part of the Olympics ever since pankration – a no-rules hybrid of boxing and wrestling where contestants occasionally died – was first introduced to the ancient games in 648 BC.

Thankfully these days combat is a more civilised affair, split into judo, wrestling, taekwondo and boxing. Winning Olympic gold is still the crowning achievement of a career for athletes in the first three, while boxers see it as a stepping-stone to greatness – Cassius Clay (before he became Muhammad Ali) and Lennox Lewis are among several successful boxers who have kicked off their professional careers from the top of the podium. Despite the points system and headgear, an impressive showing in amateur boxing is still a good predictor of potential in the pro ranks – Amir Khan and James DeGale, who demonstrates his fight training drills in this chapter, are both well on their way to the top.

Throwing leather

Success doesn't come easy, though. Boxing is one of the toughest sports in the world, demanding power, speed, coordination, agility and footwork – sometimes all at once. Judo's arguably even tougher – relaxing for a split-second can mean a swift exit, so the likes of GB's Euan Burton have to be prepared to grapple at full speed for the duration of every bout. As well as needing explosive power, high-level judo takes gazelle-like balance, ferocious grip strength and the flexibility of a gymnast – which is why you'll find some unconventional moves in Burton's workout regime. Even if you have no intention of ever stepping into the ring or on to a mat, you'll find a few classic moves to get you in fighting shape.

OLYMPIC BOXING RULES

The International Amateur Boxing Association's points scoring system

SCORING ZONES

Points are scored when a boxer lands a punch on his opponent above the belt. The blow must be landed on the white strip of the glove, the main hitting area around the knuckles. Non-scoring blows include those without the weight of the body or shoulder behind them. Illegal blows, including punches to the back of the head, kidneys and below the belt, can result in disqualification.

AWARDING A POINT

There are five ringside judges, each with a computer scoring button for each fighter. Three of the five must hit their button within one second of each other for the point to register. When boxers are fighting up close, called infighting, a point is awarded to the boxer with the best of the exchanges.

DECLARING A WINNER

The winner of a bout is the fighter with the most points, unless the fight is stopped before the final bell by the referee or by a fighter's cornerman throwing in the towel. The referee will stop the fight if one opponent stays on the floor for a count of ten, called a KO, or if there is a points difference of more than 20 after three rounds.

If points are level at the end, the best and worst total score given to each fighter by the five judges is deducted. The winner is the fighter who is left with the most points from the remaining three judges.

James DeGale

Born 3rd Feb 1986
Height 1.85m
Weight 75kg
ACHIEVEMENTS
- 2008 Gold medallist, Olympics (middleweight)
- 2008 2nd place, European amateur championships
- 2007 2nd, European amateur championships
- 2006 Bronze medallist, commonwealth Games (middleweight)

FIT FOR THE RING

Develop the knockout power and lightning speed of Olympic middleweight boxing champion James DeGale with this gym workout

PART 1
Boxing speed

'A boxer will need to spontaneously direct all his force in one direction hundreds of times during a fight, so he needs to work on explosive speed and power during training,' says DeGale's trainer Jim McDonnell. 'But it's not just about being physically explosive – in order to make best use of James's naturally fast hand and foot reaction, he has to think fast. These drills force him to do that.'

1 Blind clap punches
Sets 5 Reps 6

- Get into a boxing stance in front of a heavy bag, with your eyes closed and a training partner standing close by.
- Visualise throwing a burst of six jabs at superhuman speed. When your partner claps, open your eyes and try to do exactly that. For each rep, your partner should change the time he leaves before clapping.

DeGALE SAYS 'By thinking about speed before you start punching you're priming your body to go super-fast, and you can use this visualisation technique in the ring. The randomness of your partner's clapping keeps your reactions sharp.'

3 Skipping intervals
Sets 6 Time 30sec

- Warm up by skipping gently for 30 seconds.
- Go hard for 20 seconds, swapping between crossovers, side swings and speed steps, then skip gently for ten before taking a 30-second break.
- Once you're more confident, add double- and triple-unders.

DeGALE SAYS 'Skipping improves your timing, coordination and foot speed. These intervals prepare me for the periods of lower and higher aerobic intensity that happen in every round. The double- and triple-unders force me to jump higher, training me to be more explosive.'

2 Obstacle drills
Sets 3 Time 90sec

- Scatter six pieces of kit on the floor over a 2x2m area. Get into a boxing stance, then start moving around the obstacles, bouncing on your toes all the time, changing the direction you face after every few bounces.

- Stay light on your feet and keep changing the route you take around the pieces of kit.

DeGALE SAYS 'Developing quick, controlled footwork is vital for closing down an opponent.'

PART 2
Boxing power

'It's vital to do strength exercises that don't add bulk because that would hinder mobility,' says McDonnell. 'So we do high-volume, low-weight drills. These work the whole body because when you punch you transfer power from your legs to your core, then out through your fists, so you need whole-body strength.'

1 Bar rotations
Sets **3** Reps **20**

● In a boxing stance, hold a bar across the back of your shoulders.
● Brace your core, then, leading with your left hand, twist your body as far as you can to the left, pivoting on your feet.
● Repeat to the right. Each twist should be fast but controlled.

DeGALE SAYS 'Keeping your core braced forces your abs to transfer power between your upper and lower body, which is vital for punch strength.'

2 Fist-less shadow boxing
Sets **3** Time **1min**

● Get into a boxing stance with your fists held up to either side of your pchin.
● Keeping your hands by your head, throw jabs, uppercuts and hooks.

DeGALE SAYS 'By limiting the power you can generate from your arms, this exercise forces you to use your hips and legs to drive your punches, which makes them harder.'

3 Medicine ball single-arm press
Sets **2** Reps **10 each arm**

● Lie on the floor with your legs bent and your right hand on your right knee. Hold a small medicine ball in your left hand, your arm bent at 90˚ and palm facing up.
● Have a training partner stand above you and push down on the ball as you try to press it up.

DeGALE SAYS 'The extra resistance will help you make big strength gains in your pectorals, biceps and triceps. The result is powerful shots.'

PART 3
Agility and endurance

'Agility drills are vital for improving speed, movement around the ring and power endurance,' says McDonnell. 'A boxer needs to be able to change direction quickly and be able to throw hard shots quickly. He also needs to be able to take a serious wallop and keep going.'

1 Sweeping lunge
Sets **3** Reps **10 each leg**

- From a boxing stance, bring your back leg forward and sink into a deep lunge, sweeping your back hand forward at the same time so it almost touches the floor.
- Push off your front foot. Repeat on the other side.

DeGALE SAYS 'This strengthens the hams and glutes so you can keep bobbing and weaving throughout a fight. The sweeping adds instability, which helps to improve your balance.'

2 Bench jump combo
Sets **2** Time **1min**

- Straddle a bench, then jump up, landing with both feet on to the bench.
- Drop your left foot back to the floor.
- Hop over so your left foot is on the bench and your right on the floor, then jump up so both feet are on the bench.

DeGALE SAYS 'Doing this as fast as you can boosts strength endurance, aerobic fitness and reaction speed.'

3 Medicine ball abs slam
Sets **3** Reps **15**

- Lie on the floor in a half crunch with your fingers locked behind your head and your legs bent. Your partner should stand above you holding a medicine ball.
- Get him to throw the ball at your stomach with moderate force, catch it on the bounce and then throw again. Keep your abs braced throughout the move.

DeGALE SAYS 'Body blows are often more damaging than head shots. This will condition your abs to cope with them.'

THROWING FOR GOLD

Combining explosiveness, endurance and an iron grip is the key to being world class at judo. Top British judoka Euan Burton shares his training secrets

Euan Burton

Born 31st March 1979
Height 1.86m
Weight 81kg
ACHIEVEMENTS
● 2010, 2007 Bronze medallist, world championships

PART 1
Grip strength

'Dominating the fight for grips is such a big part of the sport now,' says Burton. 'If you're always fighting from a bad grip you're in trouble. Some guys will fight from a grip that isn't ideal because they're constantly working on techniques that can compensate for it. But as a general rule, if you win the grip fight, you're at a huge advantage.'

1 Plate flip
Sets **2**
Reps **as many as possible in 60sec**

● Hold a plate between your fingers and thumb. Rubber weight plates work best. Start with 5kg and work up.
● 'Flip' the plate and catch it. You can flip it from hand to hand or alternate hands between sets.

BURTON SAYS 'This is great for your pinch grip, which transfers really well to judo.'

2 Plate grip farmer's walk
Sets **3**
Distance **10m**

● Walk holding a weight plate in each hand.
● Keep your core braced throughout.

BURTON SAYS 'If you can use a heavy enough weight, you'll be able to feel this working your legs and core as well as your fingers.'

3 Gi pull-up
Sets **3** Reps **10**

● Throw a judo uniform (gi) or a towel over a pull-up bar.
● Hold both ends of the gi or towel as you do pull-ups. Remember: straight arms at the bottom, head as high as possible at the top.

● Add weight by holding a plate or dumb-bell between your feet.

BURTON SAYS 'If your pull strength is good enough to get someone off-balance, that's half the battle.'

PART 2
Explosive strength

'Being explosive is huge in judo,' says Burton. 'You've got to be able to go from being very relaxed into a throw as fast as possible.'

1 Zercher squat
Sets 3 Reps 5

● Stand with your feet slightly wider than shoulder-width apart and hold a barbell in the crook of your elbows.
● Start the movement by driving your hips back, and squat down until your upper thighs are parallel to the floor. Drive back up through your heels.

BURTON SAYS
'I'm working on a technique in which I drop very low, so I need to be able to explode from a really closed position. Zercher squats help this. It's also a little bit easier on your flexibility than the back squat, if your feet and ankles aren't that flexible.'

2 Single-leg step-up/ good morning
Sets 3 Reps 5 each leg

● With a barbell held in position across your shoulders, step up onto a box or bench. Raise your trailing leg and push it out in front of you.
● Now push your leg out behind you and lean forward, as you would if you were doing a good morning.
● Finally, reverse the whole move and step back down. Try this move with an empty barbell before you add weight.

BURTON SAYS 'This move is about being able to maximise the power you can generate driving through your hips off a single leg, but it's also about having control on one leg, which is crucial for a lot of throws.'

PART 3
Core work

Judo players get their core strength from sparring and sport-specific moves rather than crunches. 'A strong core is important, both for throwing and avoiding being thrown,' says Burton. 'It's part of everything you do.'

1 Windscreen wipers
Sets **3** Reps **10**

● Hang from a pull-up bar or, if you want a test of grip, a small pair of towels.
● Raise your legs, then lower them to one side and then the other, like a set of windscreen wipers.

BURTON SAYS 'This is quite an advanced move. If it's too hard at first, just bend your legs.'

2 Halo
Sets **3**
Reps **as many as possible in 30sec**

● Hold a weight plate or kettlebell in both hands, then move it in a circular motion around your head.
● Change directions after each circle.

BURTON SAYS
'Not only will this work your core in an upright position, it'll work your shoulders through a wider range of motion than you can manage in most moves.'

Cycling ›

PEDAL POWER

Use cycling drills to speed up your fitness progress

It seems hard to believe but, until relatively recently, Britain didn't have much of an Olympic cycling pedigree. In fact, we didn't win a single gold medal between a victory for Harry Ryan and Thomas Lance in the 2km tandem in the 1920 Games and Chris Boardman's gold in the 1992 pursuit (you can read Boardman's account of that victory on p148). Since then we've bagged 11 more golds and have become the team to beat, thanks to an innovative and painstaking approach to training lead by GB performance director Dave Brailsford. The GB team now wants more success inside the velodrome and on the road.

Gold rush

This section contains drills and advice from two of Britain's best cyclists. Gold medal winning track cyclist Ed Clancy goes through some of the drills that have helped him win the team pursuit. We've also got an exclusive interview with one of Britain's most successful ever Olympians, Bradley Wiggins. He has already won six medals and admits to being 'greedy' for more.

LEARN YOUR LINES

What the coloured lines on a velodrome mean

Light blue Cote d'Azur
Technically not part of the track, the blue band is used for getting riders on to the track and has a shallower incline than the rest of the track.

Black Datum line
This is 20cm above the blue band and is the fastest route around the track. It's the line taken during all timed races and record attempts.

Red Sprinters' line
This is 90cm above the black line. The area between the black and the red zone is used in sprint races and the lead rider cannot be passed on the inside when between those lines.

Dark blue Stayers' line
This line should be at least 2.5m above the inside of the track. During Madison races, team events where riders take it in turns to race, the relief riders must stay above this line until their partner links hands with them and throws them back into the race.

KING OF THE ROAD AND THE TRACK

Great Britain and Rapha team rider
Ed Clancy reveals the drills that
bagged him an Olympic gold

Ed Clancy

Born 12th March 1985
Height 1.86m
Weight 78kg
ACHIEVEMENTS
- 2011 Gold medallist, omnium, European elite championships
- 2008 Gold medallist, team pursuit, Olympics
- 2008, 2007, 2005 Gold medallist, team pursuit, world championships

PEDAL POWER

Do these drills to improve everything from intense sprints to long-distance aerobic sessions

Peak power session

You can do this session on a turbo trainer, on a track or on a road. Start with your bike in the highest gear possible. Pedal as hard as you can – a rate that, if sustained, would take you to the top of zone six (see below right) – for 15 seconds then rest for between three to five minutes. Do five reps in total.

CLANCY SAYS 'It doesn't matter if your cadence is low. You're going for maximum possible muscle recruitment. Try not to swing around. Stay low, compact and aerodynamic. If you whack it into a big gear from a standing start it's basically weightlifting on a bike.'

Threshold session

Do 15 seconds in zone six, then recover for 45 seconds at the top of zone three. Do that for eight to ten minutes for one set, and do three sets.

CLANCY SAYS 'The last four minutes should make you feel like you're going into a dark place. It's as ugly as a session gets but it's useful. If you want to get the most out of your training time, this is a very high-quality session.'

Turbo aerobic session

Ride for one minute in zone five then recover for two minutes in zone three. Do that in blocks of 15-20 minutes and complete as many blocks as you can.

CLANCY SAYS 'You can make a turbo session more aerobic and less about lactic acid tolerance by making the intervals longer. This session will develop the top end of your aerobic capacity but won't give you the same aerobic buffering as the threshold session.'

Road aerobic session

Ride in zone one or two then do blocks of 30 minutes in zone three. Do three zone three blocks in a session of about two-and-a-half hours. You can gradually build up to doing up to three hours in zone three.

CLANCY SAYS 'This is good for general aerobic conditioning. You shouldn't be dying at the end of your 30-minute block. You can go out and enjoy it, rather than sitting in a sweaty puddle on the turbo trainer.'

IN THE ZONE

All Clancy's training sessions are done in target heart rate zones. Calculate your maximum heart rate to find your own targets

Ride at 100 revolutions per minute, starting in your lowest gear. Every two minutes, move up a gear and get into as high a gear as you can manage. When you can no longer sustain the pace, measure your heart rate – that's your maximum heart rate.

ZONE 1	Up to 68%
ZONE 2	69% to 75%
ZONE 3	76% to 86%
ZONE 4	87% to 92%
ZONE 5	93% to 98%
ZONE 6	99% to 100%

CHASING THE DREAM

The three-time Olympic gold medallist Bradley Wiggins on his ambitions for 2012 and why the Tour de France will enhance his chances of glory in London

Among Britain's impressive haul of 47 medals at Beijing, 14 were won on a bike, and eight of those were gold. Two were thanks to Bradley Wiggins who brought home a bronze medal from his first Olympics in 2000, and then four years later became the first Briton in 40 years to win three medals at one games. In the run up to the 2012 Games he'll be chasing that elusive yellow jersey, but that doesn't mean the Olympic champion has given up on striking gold again.

After Britain's best year for cycling. Are we set to dominate the world?

I think we already are. We have been for a few years on the track but we're starting to do that on the road. It's been a constant progression since 2000 when Jason Queally won gold [in the men's 1km time trial] in Sydney and we keep getting stronger. I can't see it slowing down.

How has British cycling changed since the Sydney Games?

Massively. British cycling is huge now compared to what it was then. In terms of the number of people involved across the board, not just in one event, it has just got stronger. As well as on the track, the road [cyclists] are performing well, likewise with the BMX and the mountain bike.

In 2012 you'll also be competing in the Tour de France. Does this mean more to you than the Olympics?

The Olympics will always be special to me because it's where I started and where I've had most of my success. As I've switched to the road I've wanted more success and looked elsewhere for that rather than just following one path. I realise I'm capable of something else now so I'm chasing after that but also holding on to what I've had. If I'm honest I'm getting a bit greedy. I think that's just part of the motivation of the challenge to do two, seeing how far you can push yourself.

'If I'm honest I'm getting a bit greedy. That's just part of the motivation, seeing how far you can push yourself'

Will you have to adjust your training to be able to perform well in both?

We'll start throwing some extra things at the start of 2012. But the track training really complements the road in terms of endurance, and riding for three weeks really complements the track. We're very fortunate in that sense. It's not like Haile Gebrselassie trying to be a 100m sprinter. In athletics terms, this is more like going from the marathon to the 5,000m.

What's your nutrition strategy?

My nutritionist Nigel Mitchell keeps me in shape but we've learned from plenty of mistakes. After the Olympics in Athens I had a lot more upper-body bulk and I tried to burn that muscle off for the road in the space of six days. I was eating 600 calories a day and training two hours daily, putting myself in a catabolic state that meant my body was eating away muscle. Six hundred calories a day is really not a lot – it was horrible. I was wrecked at the end of it. I lost a bit of muscle but as soon as I used those muscles again it all returned. That was part of the experimental years. Learning from that has helped me in the long run.

Is there a specific goal for you on the road and track in 2012?

We've all got our individual goals. What the overall team goal is I don't know. For me it's to be up there in the Tour de France, although what 'up there' is I still don't know exactly. We all want to win bike races but it's not as simple as that for something like the Tour. For Team GB my goal is to win gold at the Olympics – without doubt.

Bradley Wiggins

Born 28th April 1980
Height 1.90m
Weight 69kg
ACHIEVEMENTS
● 2008 Gold medallist, 4km individual pursuit, Olympics
● 2008 Gold medallist, team pursuit, Olympics

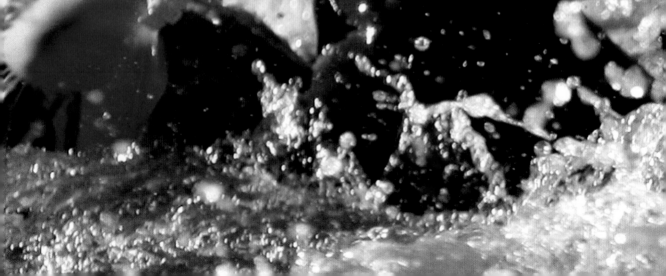

Triathlon

MULTISPORT MASTERCLASS

Use world-class training methods to smash your personal best

There are few sports in which Britain can justifiably claim to lead the world, but triathlon is one of them.

We currently have several triathlon world champions. We have the Olympic distance world champion in Alistair Brownlee (who's training drills are outlined on the next page), the world sprint triathlon champion in Jonathan Brownlee (Alistair's younger brother) and the women's Olympic distance world champion, Helen Jenkins.

We also have arguably the world's most impressive female athlete in Chrissie Wellington, a four-time world champion at the Ironman distance. The sport has also exploded at an age group level with hundreds of events taking place around the UK.

Tri training

Twenty years ago, triathlon often attracted athletes who hadn't quite made it to the top in single discipline sport. Now, however, we're seeing a generation of triathletes, such as the Brownlee brothers, who have trained specifically for the event. It's an endurance sport so the aim is to build strength without adding bulk. But to be good at triathlon you also need the explosive strength to put in a burst of pace to overtake a rival or cover a break on the bike. Follow Alistair Brownlee's drills and you'll develop all of those qualities.

TRI-ING TIMES

Here's the length of an Olympic distance triathlon, and the time it took the 2008 champion, Jan Frodeno from Germany, to complete them.

 Swim 1,500m; 18min 14sec
T1 26sec

 Bike 40km; 59min 1sec
T2 26sec

 Run 10km; 30min 46sec

Total time 1hr 48min 53sec

Alistair Brownlee

Born 23rd April 1988
Height 1.76m
Weight 62kg
ACHIEVEMENTS
- 2011, 2009 World triathlon champion
- 2008 Under-23 world triathlon champion
- 2006 Junior world triathlon champion

TRIPLE CROWN

Follow this workout from world triathlon champion Alistair Brownlee to make next season your best ever

Workout for triathlon strength and stability

1 Hang split snatch
Sets **4** Reps **4**

- Start with the bar hanging down, holding it just at the top of your thighs with your knees slightly bent.
- Pull the bar up explosively, then catch it with arms straight by sinking into a lunge.
- Bring your feet together then reset and repeat the move.

BROWNLEE SAYS 'This focuses on the eccentric muscle contraction and needs to be done quickly.'

2 Front squat to box jump
Sets **4** Reps **4**

- Perform a front squat by resting the bar on the front of your shoulders with your elbows high.
- Secure the bar, then immediately do a box jump onto a knee-high box.

BROWNLEE SAYS 'The front squat is good for your quads and hip flexors. Because it tires your legs out before you do the jump, it prepares you for going from the bike to run.'

3 Overhead barbell lunge
Sets **2** Reps **8 each side**

- Start with the barbell overhead and your core braced.
- Take a big step forwards and sink down until your knees are both bent at 90˚.
- Push through your front foot to return to the start.

BROWNLEE SAYS 'Holding the barbell overhead increases the stability element. If you have weak hips and glutes this move helps you run when you're tired after the bike.'

4 Squat jump
Sets **4** Reps **4**

- Rest the bar across your shoulders and look straight ahead.
- Sink down into a squat, then push explosively through your heels to jump.
- As you land, sink into a squat to repeat the move.

BROWNLEE SAYS 'This move combines squat strength, which is good for cycling, with the explosive power you need for running.'

Workout for triathlon strength and stability

5 Triceps extension
Sets **2** Reps **8**
each side

- Start with the dumb-bell behind your head, then straighten your arm to press the weight overhead.

BROWNLEE SAYS 'You need strong triceps for the swim – it's particularly important for the pull phase of the swim stroke.'

6 Erector spinae hold
Sets **3** Reps **8**

- Lie on a bench with your torso hanging over one end.
- Get a partner to hold your ankles, then raise your torso and hold that position for a count of two.

BROWNLEE SAYS 'This engages your glutes, lower back and hamstrings, and it is vital to have those muscles switched on for running.'

7 Isometric cycle crunch
Sets **2** Reps **to failure**

- Lie on a mat and perform an oblique crunch with one hand at your temple and the opposite leg straight out in front of you.
- Hold that position for as long as possible then repeat on the opposite side.

BROWNLEE SAYS 'In triathlon training you spend a lot of time running, which taxes your hip flexors. This move helps stabilise your hips.'

8 Single-leg bounds
Sets **2** Reps **10**
each side

- Mark out a 20m-long space then bound across it, taking off and landing on the same foot.
- Once you have completed ten bounds, turn back and repeat the move on your other leg.

BROWNLEE SAYS 'This action is like accentuated running. When you take off and land on the same foot it stabilises both your knee and your ankle.'

PERFECT BIKE MOUNT

World triathlon champion Alistair Brownlee on getting off to a flier on the bike

STEP1 **Run with the bike**
'Hold the seat in the hand that allows you to run the fastest,' says Brownlee. 'You need a fairly firm grip in case you have to change direction. In the 2008 London Triathlon people were falling all over the place in the bike transition.'

STEP2 **Prepare to jump on**
'Move your hands to the bars two or three strides before you jump on,' says Brownlee. 'If your right hand is on the seat, put your left hand on the left handlebar, let go with your right hand for a split second, then grab the bars with both hands. I find on the hoods of the handlebars is best, but do whatever gives you control.'

STEP3 **The jump**
'Make sure the bike is upright when you jump,' says Brownlee. 'You want to take off with the leg that's furthest away from the bike, so if the bike is on your right-hand side take off with your left leg. Lift your right leg as it goes around the back of the saddle while your left leg comes in towards the bike.'

STEP4 **Start to pedal**
'Aim to land on your backside or on the inside of your thigh,' says Brownlee. 'The next thing is to put your feet on – not in – your shoes, which should be attached to your pedals. Usually you pedal for a bit until the race is stable, then slip your feet into your shoes.'

HIT NEW HEIGHTS

To keep improving your performance, you need to strive to reach new levels of fitness. Test yourself against former world triathlon champion Tim Don

Whether you're an elite-level athlete or a club runner, the key to staying motivated and feeling positive is to keep improving your race performance and moving higher and higher in the finishing positions.

'If you're going to hit your training targets, you can't slack off – you must strive to get fitter and faster,' says elite triathlete Tim Don. 'Only through sustained effort will you be able to tap into your reserves as your competitors are starting to run on empty, and this holds

true whatever your discipline or race distance. You can never afford to rest on your laurels. Even world record holders want to chip away at their best ever efforts. Pushing yourself hard in training so you can push yourself even harder in races is the only way to maintain improvement. And who doesn't want to finish fast?

'So here are some pretty good benchmarks for you to measure your performance against – they're my personal best times for 1,500m swimming, 40km cycle and 10km run. And I've got some useful target times and tips to help you get faster for each one as well.'

> 'You can't slack off – you must strive to get fitter and faster constantly'

YOUR TARGET IS...

The goals you should aim for in each discipline – and how to achieve them

1,500m pool swim
Tim Don's PB **17min 9sec**

Excellent	25min
Good	30min
Average	40min

'With swimming it is definitely worth investing a few quid for a one-on-one session with a good coach,' says Don. 'You may need only one hour with them to eliminate any fundamental flaws in your technique that could be costing you minutes, let alone seconds. If you're confident your form is already pretty good, then you should bear this in mind: don't get hung up on using your legs. They account for as little as ten per cent of forward movement. Keep your legs close together and as straight as you can and focus on rotating your torso effectively for maximum efficiency through each stroke.'

40km bike
Tim Don's PB **55min 43sec**

Excellent	1hr
Good	1hr 10m
Average	1hr 20m

'Cycling speed is about power and efficiency,' says Don. 'The quickest way to get faster is to ensure your bike is properly set up to suit your body. If you are unsure go to a specialist cycle shop, but there are some key things that anyone can do at home to make sure they're cycling efficiently. With the pedal at its lowest point, your heel should rest on it with only a very slight bend in your knee; keep your upper body relaxed while your legs pump and don't sway from side to side; keep cadence between 90 and 100rpm; get clipless pedals because you'll instantly go faster; and go easy on the brakes.'

10km run
Tim Don's PB 28min 56sec*

Excellent	**40min**
Good	**45min**
Average	**50min**

*road race

'The only way to improve your 10km time is to train outside of your comfort zone – whether it's intervals, hill runs or race pace sessions,' says Don. 'This is the only guaranteed method to improve your speed endurance levels so you can kick on in the race when the going gets tough.

'I'd even advise doing some off-road or cross-country races and some half-marathons to improve your leg strength, cardiovascular system and break up the boredom of doing short, all-out sessions.

'The most important thing with all of these tips is that they're not just something to try once. Keep at it and your fitness, and times, will keep improving.'

Gymnastics ⟩

RING MASTERS

Use bodyweight moves to build a gymnast's body

Gymnastics is a sport where Britain has come from nowhere to produce a crop of medal hopefuls. Dominating the men's evens are 22-year-old Louis Smith and 21-year-old Dan Keatings and you can follow drills from both athletes on the following pages.

Their events are all about controlling bodyweight, which means that a lot of their training is done using bodyweight alone. That's particularly useful for anyone who wants to train at home and doesn't have much kit because as this sport proves you don't need to have lots of fancy kit to build an incredible body.

JOY OF SIX

Here's what's involved in the half-dozen all-around disciplines

In the all-around finals (abbreviated AA), the gymnasts are individual competitors and perform on all six apparatus. Their scores from all six events are added together and the gymnasts with the three highest totals are awarded all-around medals. Only two gymnasts from each country may advance to the all-around finals.

Vault
A gymnast sprints down a 25m runway, leaping from a spring board hands first towards the vault and 'popping' off into a series of rotations finishing in a controlled landing.

Pommel horse
The routine should be a smooth continuous chain of circular and pendulum type swings, double leg circles, scissor movements and undercuts using all parts of the horse, finishing with a dismount.

Parallel bars
Gymnasts travel along and work both above and below bars just wider than shoulder-width apart, executing swings, balances, static strength holds and releases.

Rings
Arguably the most physically demanding event. Rings are suspended 2.8m above the floor and gymnasts must perform static strength moves and a dynamic display while preventing the rings from swinging.

Floor exercise
Performed on a 12x12m sprung floor, gymnasts must touch each corner once and show a personal touch of expression in combining somersaults, twists, leaps for between 60-70 seconds.

Horizontal high bar
The bar must not be touched by the gymnast's body and should demonstrate changes in grip, movements forward and backward, plus release and re-grasp of the bar, finished with a spectacular dismount.

Daniel Keatings
Born 4th January 1990
Height 1.71m
Weight 66kg
ACHIEVEMENTS
● 2010 Gold medallist
(pommel horse), silver
medallist (team
competition), European
championships
● 2009 Silver
medallist (all-around
competition), world
championships

HORSE POWER

Build strength and agility with Daniel
Keatings's tough bodyweight drills

PART 1
Explosive power

'We'll do about an hour and a half of conditioning in total each day, on top of specific training on the apparatus,' says Keatings. 'Power is one of the most important things to train, because every discipline has an explosive element.'

1 Parallel press-up
Sets **3** Reps **5**

- Using a set of parallettes – press-up bars will do at a push – set them roughly shoulder-width apart.
- Start with your hands between them and do an explosive press-up, landing with your hands on the bars. Do another press-up and land with your hands outside the bars. Now go back to the bars, then back to the centre. That's four press-ups and one rep.

KEATINGS SAYS 'This builds explosive power but also coordination – you have to get used to catching those bars.'

2 Muscle-up
Sets **2** Reps **5**

- Start by hanging from a set of rings with a high grip – the heel of your palms should be resting on the rings.
- Perform an explosive pull-up and, as your chest passes the rings, transition into a dip to push yourself above them. Driving your chest forward will help.

KEATINGS SAYS 'Some people do this with a leg swing but you'll get stronger if you make the technique clean. You wouldn't swing your legs in a gymnastics routine.'

PART 2
Strength endurance

'You don't need much cardio to get through a minute-long routine,' says Keatings. 'But you do need to have the strength to get through every move. We train twice a day and we'll generally fit some of these conditioning moves in after each session. They also include a bit of skill work.'

1 Straight arm hop
Sets 2 Reps 12

● Start in a press-up position with your hands on a platform roughly 10cm off the ground.
● Keeping your elbows locked, use your wrists and shoulders to bounce down to the ground and then quickly back to the platform. This isn't a press-up. If you get really confident, try it with elevated feet.

KEATINGS SAYS 'This builds strength in your wrists and shoulders – lots of gymnastic moves involve catching yourself on straight arms.'

2 Dish rock
Sets 2 Reps 20

● Form a dish shape by bending slightly at the waist, and hold it as you rock backwards and forwards.
● Stay solid and pivot on your lower back.

KEATINGS SAYS 'You need to get used to holding this shape and keeping a strong core while you're tumbling.'

3 Front raise
Sets 3 Reps 10

● With a weight plate held in both hands, explosively raise it above your head.
● Don't try and rock backwards to make the move easier – stand against a wall or bench so you are not using your lower back.

KEATINGS SAYS 'Gymnastics is about opening and closing your shoulders quickly, so we'll do these quite explosively.'

PART 3
Core strength

'Keeping a tight core is crucial in gymnastics,' says Keatings. 'It will give you more spring when you're tumbling. We don't really do sit-ups – instead, we do moves that emphasise keeping everything rigid. Even a solid handstand will work your core harder than a sit-up. We'll throw in these moves whenever we can – as a warm-up, or to finish a session.'

1 Gym ball rollout
Sets **3** Reps **12**

● Support yourself in a press-up position with your shins on a gym ball. Keep your body in a straight line and your core tight.
● Keeping your hands in the same place, roll yourself backwards until the ball is under your hips. Use your shoulders to pull yourself back to the start position.

KEATINGS SAYS 'This is about keeping a strong core, which is important on the bars and in floorwork.'

2 Gym ball bridge
Sets **3** Reps **12**

● Lie on your shoulders with both feet on a gym ball.
● Bridge up as explosively as possible, and repeat.

KEATINGS SAYS 'This works on your glutes and core stability in the opposite direction from the rollouts.'

SPRING INTO ACTION

Britain's Olympic medallist Louis Smith demonstrates the moves that will help you build an awesome physique

Louis Smith

Born 22nd April 1989
Height 1.79m
Weight 76kg
ACHIEVEMENTS
● 2008 Bronze medallist (pommel horse), Olympics
● 2006 Gold medallist, Commonwealth games
● 2004, 2006 European junior champion

Workout for gymnastics strength

1 Dish rock
Sets **3** Reps **8**

● Lie flat, arms and legs extended, then crunch your arms and legs up and lock them into position.
● Rock your weight backwards and forwards onto your hips and then your shoulders.
● Hold the rocker position for eight seconds at the end.

SMITH SAYS 'This combination move trains the core with its static hold aspect and then targets the abs with the rocking motion for a strong midsection.'

2 Handstand dip
Sets **2** Reps **10 first set, 7 second set**

● Ask a training partner to assist you into a handstand and to hold your ankles during the move.
● Lock your core to maintain your body shape and bend your elbows to lower down.
● Lean your body to balance your weight, but don't bend at the hips.

SMITH SAYS 'A great exercise for conditioning your biceps and triceps dynamically while keeping your balance in an inverted position. You can build up to it with easier versions, placing your feet at various inclines rather than in a handstand.'

3 Rebound jumps
Sets **6** Reps **3**

- Set three benches or markers with enough distance between to allow a two-footed leap.
- Bend your knees and swing your arms back before doing a two-footed take-off. When you jump, bring your arms up and knees in to your chest.

- Land on two feet, bending your knees, then explode immediately into the next jump.

SMITH SAYS 'This plyometric drill gives legs dynamic spring – essential for tumbling skills.'

4 Jump and squat
Sets **3** Reps **8**

- From standing, bend your knees and explode into a forward jump, going for length rather than height.
- Bend your knees as you land and then continue this into a squat with thighs parallel to the floor, and hold for one second.
- Drive back up and fully engage your glutes as you go into the next jump.

SMITH SAYS 'When you land after jumping from the pommel horse it has to be with no discernable movement, so this exercise is great. It's also good for improving knee stability and helping to prevent injury.'

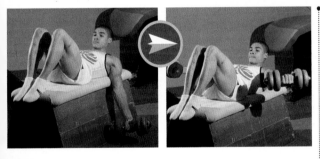

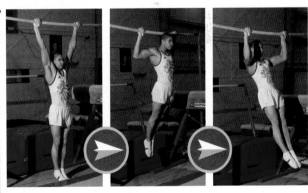

5 Straight-arm lift
Sets **3** Reps **10**

- Holding a dumb-bell in each hand, lie back and take the arch out of your lower back by lifting your head slightly.
- Keeping your arms straight, lift them up towards the ceiling, palms facing upwards.
- Pause for one second and lower, maintaining tension in your arms.

SMITH SAYS 'This develops static strength in your arms, allowing you to shift position on the rings and keep his arms straight on the other apparatus.'

6 Winger
Sets **3** Reps **5**

- Do a pull-up until your upper arms are parallel to the bar.
- Keeping your upper arms level, move your body forwards and backwards quickly.
- Maintain the tension in your upper body to stay up near the bar.

SMITH SAYS 'Both the pectorals and the upper back muscles will be specifically targeted by this move, which combines isometric and dynamic elements for overall strength.'

Legends ›

SOLID GOLD PERFORMANCES

Home athletes competing in the Olympics will have the chance to secure their status as British sporting legends. But how do you win a gold medal and what's it like to perform with the hopes of the nation resting on your well-trained shoulders? Five athletes speak about the success they achieved on the biggest stage.

STEVE REDGRAVE

Britain's greatest ever Olympian has won more gold medals than anyone else

BORN
22nd March 1962

OLYMPIC MEDALS
Gold coxed four,
1984 Los Angeles

Gold coxless pair,
1988 Seoul

Gold coxless pair,
1992 Barcelona

Gold coxless pair,
1996 Atlanta

Gold coxless four,
2000 Sydney

Bronze coxed pair,
1988 Seoul

'**A**nyone who sees me go anywhere near a boat again, ever, you've got my permission to shoot me.'
That's what a breathless Redgrave said moments after chalking up Olympic gold number four in 1996 and it's an insight into the physical demands of what he calls a 'purely fitness sport'. Thankfully no one took him literally, and he was back in an Olympic final four years later as part of a coxless four that included Matthew Pinsent, James Cracknell and Tim Foster. Their boat beat Italy by just 0.38 seconds, prompting a tearful Pinsent to clamber over Foster and embrace Britain's only five-time gold medal winner.

Which of your victories was the most significant?
The last one has got to be the defining one. It was the one that captured the public's imagination. I remember going to a speaking engagement soon after the games. I walked into the room and there was a standing ovation. I thought, somebody important must have walked in and looked round to see who it was. And it was me. That was weird.

Did all the victories feel similar?
Pretty similar. The first one was just relief because we became favourites two months beforehand so there was a lot of pressure. Then in Sydney, even though I'd already won four gold medals, if I hadn't been successful, that's how I'd have been perceived – good career but failed at the end.

What made you so good?
At the start of my career I had a belief that I could be one of the world's best rowers. There wasn't a lot of evidence behind that but I went into my career with this belief that I could win races and that carries you a long way. Then after that first Olympic gold, I knew I could do it and you think, why can't I do it again? But you have to reinvent yourself every time because staying at the same level isn't going to be good enough to win.

Did you train harder or smarter than the competition?
Maybe a bit of both. We did train hard. The old British way of doing it was short, sharp, very intensive. There were rumours that the East Germans were putting in extra hours after training and you thought, how could they do that without being fatigued all the time? But they would train at a lower intensity. When I started doing more volume that's when the results started coming – but I still had the mentality of keeping the intensity. So I was doing more volume and more intensity than the East Germans. That's what helped me leapfrog over some of the other nations.

What has been biggest change to the sport since you competed?
More time in the boat, more time training and a much more professional attitude than in the 1970s and 1980s. The training isn't that much different but there is an overall ethos that every aspect is important. Now athletes are preparing a lot more off the water.

Would you do anything to change the way you trained?
I'd have liked to have learned from older athletes about how they'd been able to improve, but there used to be a culture of people keeping their cards close to their chest. I was seen as a threat to some of the older people on the team rather than someone to whom they could give a helping hand. That's changed; now there's more of a team ethic.

How important was your partnership with Matthew Pinsent?
It's not just a partnership; You become a very close unit. Matt and I spent at lot of time together before Atlanta and we'd be aware when the other one was maybe struggling a little bit with nerves, so we'd change the conversation away from racing and towards something more lighthearted.

What advice would you give to an athlete taking part in 2012?
The closer you get the more nerve wracking it becomes. But you need your nerves. You need the adrenaline pumping. It can feel horrible but the butterflies in your stomach can be an advantage, not a disadvantage.

'We did train hard. The old British way of doing it was short, sharp, very intensive'

SEB COE

Britain's most successful Olympic middle distance runner now heads the 2012 organising team

BORN
29th September 1956

OLYMPIC MEDALS

Gold 1,500m,
1980 Moscow

Gold 1,500m,
1984 Los Angeles

Silver 800m,
1980 Moscow

Silver 800m,
1984 Los Angeles

Coe entered the 1980 Moscow Olympics as the 800m world record holder but in the final he left himself with a lot of ground to make up in the home straight.

He tried to kick for the front but had to settle for silver behind his fierce rival Steve Ovett. A few days later the pair met again in the final of the 1,500m, a distance over which Ovett had been undefeated for three years. This time Coe judged his pace perfectly, storming to the front on the final bend to win his first gold at a major championship.

After suffering from a career threatening illness in 1983 Coe won silver again in the 800m at the 1984 Los Angeles Olympics. In the 1,500m final

'The overwhelming feeling when you win is not "I'm Olympic champion". It's relief'

the young British runner Steve Cram, who was the reigning world champion at that distance, was breathing down Coe's neck with 200m to go. Cram pushed his team-mate all the way but it was Coe who crossed the line in new world record time of 3.32.53. He's since experienced a different Olympic success as head of the London 2012 bid, and is chairman of the Games' organising committee.

What are your defining moments of your victories?
The overwhelming feeling when you finish is not, 'that's fantastic, I've become an Olympic champion', it's 'thank God I've got through it'. It's relief. And the relief is

twofold, firstly because it's hard work and secondly there's relief that you haven't let down your friends and family.

What's the key to Olympic success?
It's about maintaining extraordinary levels of focus for when it matters, then being able to switch off, and then switch on again. The final is an extraordinary moment but you think of it as a campaign. In Los Angeles I had seven races in nine days. It's a war of attrition. You prepare, you get though and then do the same thing the next day. In an Olympic competition you're buying your ticket station to station.

How did you cope with the pressure of the Olympics?
I was at my most confident, mentally, when I knew that physically I was in fantastic shape. So I think that mental strength comes from the knowledge that physically you've left no stone unturned in training. I never finished the hardest race feeling even three quarters as tired as I did from the average training session, and I think that's important. That gives you mental strength.

What made you better than everyone else?
It think it probably had a lot to do with the genetic lottery of life. I had a great coach and I think I was able to focus. And I enjoyed what I did. I wasn't dragged into track and field. I think that's important. You can't force kids to do something they don't want to do.

What's the atmosphere like in the village?
Fantastic. I've got friends I met in the village, both inside the British team and outside of the British team who

are still friends of mine from Los Angeles. Some of the strongest friendships are made in sport.

What makes a great Olympian?
Nothing in sport happens overnight. And there are days when you just do things that you have to do. I'm not going to tell you that every training session is a joy. Road work at 6.30am, when you can hardly move your hands because it's so cold, that isn't an enjoyable experience but it's what you have to go through if you want to win medals.

What advice would you have to athletes competing in 2012?
My advice to athletes competing in London – given that the village is so accessible and is next to the park – is to stay in the village. In Los Angeles, a lot of the athletes stayed out. A lot of my main competitors stayed in hotels. But I stayed in the village with Daley [Thompson] and we always look back on that as the smartest thing we did. I had the food. I had the transport system. I had the management. If I came back from a race that ended late and needed a massage I could still get one at two in the morning.

What's the difference between the Olympics and other major competitions?
They're different planets. If you were to say to an athlete, 'I'm going to give you the opportunity to compete in a world championship and an Olympic games, but you can only win one of them, which will it be?' I can guarantee that 100 times out of 100 that athlete will say the Olympic games because it has the cachet. Mentally and physically it's the toughest environment to navigate your way through.

LINFORD CHRISTIE

Britain's fastest ever man over 100m on why he knew he was going to win gold

BORN
2nd April 1960

OLYMPIC MEDALS
Gold 100m,
1992 Barcelona

Silver 100m,
1988 Seoul

Silver 4x100m relay,
1988 Seoul

Christie crossed the line in third place in the 100m final at the 1988 Olympics but was upgraded to a silver medal behind Carl Lewis after Canadian Ben Johnson was disqualified for doping. He followed that up by running the anchor leg in the 4x100m relay final, in which the GB team came second.

Four years later in Barcelona, Christie's main threat was another American – the former world record holder, Leroy Burrell. He was seven years younger than Christie and the fastest man in the final but it was the Briton who got out of the blocks first. Burrell couldn't claw his way back into the race and Christie stormed home to win in 9.97.

Since retiring from competition Christie has become a coach, and is training Olympic hopefuls such as 100m runner Mark Lewis-Francis.

What's your defining memory of the final in 1992?
I knew I was going to win. I beat Leroy Burrell in the semi-finals and he was the guy who I thought was going to be my main rival. From the way we both ran I knew I could have gone past him at any time in the race.

Having won silver in Seoul, did you feel under pressure in Barcelona?
I never really felt pressure. Pressure is something you put on yourself or you allow other people to put on you. I just tried to go out there and enjoy it and I always felt that I could do whatever it would take to win the race.

How do the Olympics differ from world championships?
It's the Olympic title that everyone wants. You can win everything else but if you haven't got an Olympic title you're not really recognised as one of the greats. But I actually enjoyed my world championship victory [in 1993] more than the Olympics because it was a tougher race and I had to run 9.87 to win [a British record that still stands].

What's the atmosphere like in the Olympic village?
The atmosphere is great. Once the guy says 'on your marks', then everything goes quiet but until that time, I'd be having a laugh. It kept me relaxed. Some athletes start thinking about the race days before but that's just a waste of adrenaline and nervous energy that you could use during the race.

How has the sport changed since you were running?
The biggest change is that people are running faster. The world record hasn't just been shaved, it has been chopped up. In my day, someone would run 9.93, then 9.91 then 9.90. It just came down in bits. But

Usain [Bolt] didn't even go into the 9.60s. He just went straight to 9.58. A long time ago someone asked me how fast I think man will go and I said 9.5 seconds. People thought I was a quack back then.

Can it go lower?
I think it can. I think Usain will take it down a little bit. And once he has done that, people will think, 'right, this is what we have to do to be in with a chance of winning a medal'. They'll up their training and up their games. It used to be that running sub-ten was a peak performance. Now you run 9.9 seconds and you won't even make the final of the Olympics because there are so many people running quickly.

What advice would you give to athletes competing in 2012?
Once you make the final, all the sheets are wiped clean. You have to think that you can do it. Don't worry about the time people are running before they get to you. Worry about the time they do when they race against you.

Follow Linford Christie on Twitter at @ ChristieLinford.

'It's the Olympic title everyone wants. Without it you're not really one of the greats'

CHRIS BOARDMAN

His gold at Barcelona in 1992 paved the
way for future British cycling success

BORN
26th August 1968

OLYMPIC MEDALS
Gold individual pursuit,
1992 Barcelona

Bronze 52km time trial,
1996 Atlanta

While he was progressing through the rounds of the individual time trial, a 4km track event, at the 1992 Olympics, Boardman received less attention than his Lotus-designed uni-axle 'SuperBike'. So distinct was the bike that some commentators suggested it was the futuristic carbon-fibre frame, rather than the man riding it, that was responsible for the Briton's speed. But Boardman's performance in the final was so immense that the man he beat, German rider Jens Lehmann, was in no doubt about what was behind the result. 'People say, was it the bike or was it the man?' Lehmann said after the race. 'I can tell you it was the man.'

What's your defining memory of your victory?

It's a blur, really. I was an unemployed carpenter from Hoylake and before the final I knew that the next four and half minutes could change my life. So there was an immense sense of relief to have not screwed it up.

Did you enjoy it?

No. Not me. I'm sure there are people with a different mental approach but I'm afraid I'm a fear of failure kind of person. I look for the threats and put all my energy into stopping those

things getting in the way. It's a rather negative outlook but it was effective.

Were you nervous?

Being able to cope with the enormity of the situation is very important. You can have the best physical capability in the world but if you can't put it down at a given moment then you're not going to maximise your potential. The way to learn how to do that, for most people, is to fail. You learn from that failure.

How did you deal with the pressure?

A good friend of mine, a psychologist called John Sire, sat with me the hour before the final. He said, 'what is it that scares you? What is it that worries you?' We talked through lots of stuff and in the end I said, 'sod it. I'm just going to be as good as I can be and see where it'll get me.' He just looked at me and smiled, in that way psychologists do. He had given me that anchoring thought. A good psychologist doesn't tell you anything, but they do ask the right questions.

What's the key to Olympic success?

You can have the best physical capability in the world but if you can't put it down at a given moment then you're not going to maximise your potential. I boiled it down to not trying to win an Olympic gold medal, just trying to be as good as I could be. If you try to win a medal, there are a lot of things that can happen on the other side of the track that are outside your control.

What's the atmosphere in the athletes' village like?

Great fun for those who have finished. But for those who are still competing it's like a large-scale dentist's waiting room.

> 'I wasn't trying
> to win an Olympic
> gold medal, just
> be as good as
> I could be'

Have you always been meticulous in your approach to preparation?

Yeah. I'm fascinated by detail and understanding how things work. And then trying to improve it and examining results. The common terminology is called reflective practise.

Would you change anything about the way you trained?

I should have addressed the psychological side of it more deeply because I tended to avoid threats. I never really focused on winning road races because I couldn't control all the variables. That was quite a sad approach, really. There were missed opportunities because I only looked for the threats rather than the opportunities. Learning to have a more positive attitude would be the one thing I'd change.

What advice would you give to an athlete competing in London 2012?

I would ask them a question that would get them to focus on what they can do, rather than the things that scare them. That's what was done for me and it was a fantastic, insightful thing that John Sire did – getting me to focus on something that I could hang on to, no matter how much stress there was.

JONATHAN EDWARDS

The man who won triple jump gold in Sydney was so good that his world record still stands

BORN
10th May 1966

OLYMPIC MEDALS
Gold triple jump,
2000 Sydney

Silver triple jump,
1996 Atlanta

In the second round of the 1995 world championships in Gothenburg, Sweden, Edwards hopped, skipped and jumped an incredible 18.29m to set a new triple jump world record. That leap made him favourite to win Olympic gold in Atlanta the following year, where he produced a jump of 17.88. Unfortunately, the American Kenny Harrison was also on form and jumped 18.09m, leaving Edwards with a silver medal. Four years later in Sydney, at his last Olympic games, he was in second place after two rounds and it looked as though he might again miss out again on gold. Then in the third round he managed a jump of 17.71m – shorter than in Atlanta but the longest jump of the competition. Since hanging up his spikes Edwards has become an athletics commentator for the BBC.

What was your defining memory from your victory in Sydney?
My defining memory from that day was watching Cathy Freeman [the Australian 400m runner] win, rather than me winning. I think everyone that night felt like a bit of a sideshow.

Did that make it more special?
In some ways it was less, because I didn't get as much attention. But then the fact that I competed on 'magic Monday', probably more people do remember it.

> 'I knew that being able to win and winning were two very different things'

How did coming second in Atlanta affect your approach to Sydney?
In Atlanta I was under pressure, I was the red-hot favourite and the Olympic games was a new experience. When I got to Sydney there was no negative hangover from thinking that I was the favourite in 1996 and I messed it up. This was my last chance to win at the Olympics. Having broken the world record and become world champion there was a lot of pressure to round my career off in what felt like the right way.

How did that pressure affect you?
I was never the most positive thinker leading up to a competition. I'd have all sorts of doubts, fears and insecurities. But I learned over the years that they didn't really affect my performance so I didn't get too worked up about the fact that I didn't feel confident. Between jumps I didn't sit or lie. I just paced. I was full of nervous energy. I might watch what other competitors were doing but mostly I was just preparing, but not in a particularly structured way.

How did you deal with pressure?
I had a good team around me. And back then my faith was very important to me. It gave me a framework for dealing with winning and losing and a sense of perspective. It wasn't all about being the best triple jumper in the world. It was about using my talent because it was something that God had given to me.

Would not having a belief in God have affected your performances?
It would certainly have felt different, without a Christian faith. As to whether I'd have jumped any differently, I think my gut feeling would be no. Physically, I was capable of doing it. So had I not had that faith I would have done it in a different way. But that said, it helped me no end. Bluntly, it worked.

What was the key to your victory in Sydney?
I was in good shape. There's no amount of mental preparation or wanting to win that can disguise the fact that you're not in the best of shape. I managed my way through the competition well, considering there was so much else going on in the stadium. I got a decent jump out in the 3rd round. I was jumping last so I had a chance to respond to whatever anybody else was doing.

Did you know you would win?
I didn't know. I knew I could win because at my best I was better than anyone else. But I had lost an Olympic final and two world championship finals since breaking the world record, so I knew that being able to win and winning were two very different things.

Has the event moved on?
There are a number of men's field event records from the 1990s that aren't being challenged: men's long jump, men's javelin, men's high jump, my triple jump record. So you could say that, in some respects, the event hasn't moved on.

Who do you think will win the triple jump in London?
At this stage, [British triple jumper] Phillips Idowu. But I might yet change my prediction.

Watch the action >

Athletics
Where Olympic Stadium –
Olympic Park (track, field
and combined events);
The Mall (road events)
When Friday 3rd August –
Sunday 12th August
Medal events 47
Athletes 2,000

Archery
Where Lord's Cricket Ground
When Friday 27th July – Friday 3rd August
Medal events 4
Athletes 128 (64 men, 64 women)

Badminton
Where Wembley Arena
When Saturday 28th July – Sunday 5th August
Medal events 5
Athletes 172

Basketball
Where Basketball Arena, Olympic Park; North Greenwich Arena
When Saturday 28th July – Sunday 12th August
Medal events 2
Athletes 288 (144 men, 144 women, 2 x 12 teams)

Beach volleyball
Where Horse Guards Parade
When Saturday 28th July – Thursday 9th August
Medal events 2
Athletes 96 (48 men, 48 women; 2 x 24 teams)

Boxing
Where ExCeL
When Saturday 28th July – Sunday 12th August
Medal events 13
Athletes 286 (250 men, 36 women)

Canoe sprint
Where Eton Dorney
When Monday 6th August – Saturday 11th August
Medals events 12
Athletes 248

Cycling, BMX
Where BMX Track, Olympic Park
When Wednesday 8 – Friday 10 August
Medal events 2
Athletes 48

Cycling, mountain bike
Where Hadleigh Farm, Essex
When Saturday 11th – Sunday 12th August
Medal events 2
Athletes 80 (50 men, 30 women)

Canoe Slalom
Where Lee Valley White Water Centre
When Sunday 29th July – Thursday 2nd August
Medal Events 4
Athletes 82

Diving
Where Aquatics Centre, Olympic Park
When Sunday 29th July – Saturday 11th August
Medal events 8
Athletes 136 (68 men, 68 women)

Cycling, track
Where Velodrome
When Thursday 2nd – Tuesday 7th August
Medal events 10
Athletes 188 (104 men, 84 women)

Equestrian dressage
Where Greenwich Park
When Thursday 2nd – Thursday 9th August
Medal Events 2
Athletes 50

Equestrian eventing
Where Greenwich Park
When Saturday 28th July – Tuesday 31st July
Medal events 2
Athletes 75

Equestrian jumping
Where Greenwich Park
When Saturday 4th – Wednesday 8th August
Medal events 2
Athletes 75

Fencing
Where ExCeL
When Saturday 28th July – Sunday 5th August
Medal events 10
Athletes 212

Gymnastics rhythmic
Where Wembley Arena
When Thursday 9th August – Sun 12th August
Medal events 2
Athletes 96 (all women)

Football
Where City of Coventry Stadium (Coventry), Hampden Park (Glasgow), Millennium Stadium (Cardiff), Old Trafford (Manchester), St James' Park (Newcastle), Wembley Stadium
When Wednesday 25th July – Saturday 11th August
Medal events 2
Athletes 504 (288 men, 216 women; 16 men's teams, 12 women's teams)

Cycling, road
Where The Mall (road race); Hampton Court Palace (time trial)
When Saturday 28th July – Wednesday 1st August
Medal events 4
Athletes 212 (145 men, 67 women)

Gymnastics, artistic

Where North Greenwich Arena
When Saturday 28th July – Tuesday 7th August
Medal events 14
Athletes 196 (98 men, 98 women)

Gymnastics trampoline
Where North Greenwich Arena
When Friday 3rd August – Saturday 4th August
Medal events 2
Athletes 32

Judo
Where ExCeL
When Saturday 28th July – Friday 3rd August
Medal Events 14
Athletes 386

Hockey
Where Hockey Centre, Olympic Park
When Sunday 29th July – Saturday 11th August
Medal events 2
Athletes 384 (192 men, 192 women; 2 x 12 teams)

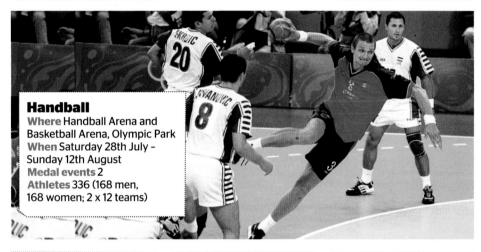

Handball
Where Handball Arena and Basketball Arena, Olympic Park
When Saturday 28th July – Sunday 12th August
Medal events 2
Athletes 336 (168 men, 168 women; 2 x 12 teams)

Modern pentathlon
Where Handball Arena, Aquatics Centre, Greenwich Park
When Saturday 11th August – Sun 12th August
Medal events 2
Athletes 72 (36 men, 36 women)

Rowing
Where Eton Dorney
When Saturday 28th July – Sunday 4th August
Medal events 14
Athletes 550 (353 men, 197 women)

Sailing
Venue Weymouth Bay and Portland Harbour
Dates Sunday 29th July – Saturday 11th August
Medal events 10
Athletes 380 (237 men, 143 women)

Swimming
Where Aquatics Centre, Olympic Park (pool events); Hyde Park (marathon swimming, 10km)
When Saturday 28th July – Friday 10th August
Medal events 34
Athletes 950

Shooting
Where The Royal Artillery Barracks
When Saturday 28th July – Monday 6th August
Medal events 15
Athletes 390

Tae kwon do
Where ExCeL
When Wednesday 8th August – Saturday 11th August
Medal events 8
Athletes 128 (64 men, 64 women)

Synchronised swimming
Where Aquatics Centre – Olympic Park
When Sunday 5th August – Friday 10th August
Medal events 2
Athletes 104 (all women)

Table tennis
Where ExCeL
When Saturday 28th July – Wednesday 8th August
Medal events 4
Athletes 172 (86 men, 86 women)

Tennis
Where Wimbledon
When Saturday 28th July – Sunday 5th August
Medal events 5
Athletes 172 (86 men, 86 women)

Water polo
Where Water Polo Arena, Olympic Park
When Sunday 29th July – Sunday 12th August
Medal events 2
Athletes 260 (156 men, 104 women)

Volleyball
Where Earls Court
When Saturday 28th July – Sunday 12th August
Medal events 2
Athletes 288 (144 men, 144 women; 2 x 12 teams)

Wrestling
Where ExCeL
When Sunday 5th August – Sunday 12th August
Medal events 18
Athletes 344 (272 men, 72 women)

Triathlon
Where Hyde Park
When Saturday 4th August and Tuesday 7th August
Medal events 2
Athletes 110 (55 men, 55 women)

Weightlifting
Where ExCeL
When Saturday 28th July
– Tuesday 7th August
Medal events 15
Athletes 260 (156 men,
104 women)